Dec

Guy, Huw, Trish and Mick

For their loving support

and to

Gary

because I, at least, always keep my promises

By the same author, also from Capall Bann:

The Eildon Tree - Romany Language and Lore

Acknowledgements

Oubliette made much of its first appearance as the short story Prologue published by Roy and Beryl Brodrick in the magazine Bona in 1975. I am grateful to them.

I am grateful to Mr Gordon Boswell forn the times he spent talking to me about Romany life on my frequent visits to his splendid Romany Museum at Spalding in Lincolnshire.

I am very grateful to Caroline Martin who has helped me to prepare this book for publication.

Contents

Chapter One   Lifting the Latch   7
Chapter Two   A Romany History and a Short One   24
Chapter Three   Some Romany Customs and Lore   30
Chapter Four   Romany Remedies   40
A Note on Romany Measures   41
Asthma and Other Chest Complaints   42
Baldness   42
Balm (Romany Balm)   42
Beauty Ointment (Face Cream)   42
Beauty Cream (Called Gipsy Beauty Cream)   43
Bladder Ailments   43
Blood Pressure   43
Boils and Skin Inflamations   43
Catarrh   44
Chest Complaints and Hacking Coughs   44
Chilblains   44
Constipation   45
Coughs   45
Cystitis   45
Diarrhoea   45
Foot Ointment (Gipsy Foot Ointment)   46
Gastritis   46
Gout   46
Hair Stimulant   47
Headaches and Neuralgia   47
Herb Beer   47
Hoarseness   48
Horehound and Wormwood Tonic Beer   48
Indigestion   48
Isinglass   48
Insomnia   49

Kidney Tonic 49
Menstrual Irregularities 49
Menstruation - Suppressed 49
Nasal Congestion and Head Colds 49
Nerves 50
Obesity 50
Piles 50
Pleurisy 51
Rheumatism 51
Sciatica 51
Sickness and Flatulence 51
Sore Throats 51
Sprains, Muscular Aches and Pains 51
Tonic Stout 52
Ulcers (external) 52
Urinary Complaints 52
Warts, Boils, Cold Sores and Ulcers 53
Wounds and Sores 53
Chapter Five   Appleby Horse Fair 55
Chapter Six   Romany Vet, Romany Poacher 63
The Romany Horse 63
Broken-Wind (asthma in horses) 63
Bog Spavin 63
Colic 65
Coughs 65
Cracked Heels 65
Mange 65
Quittor (a disease of the foot) 65
Sprains and Sores 65
Staggers (a stomach disorder) 66
Thrush (foot thrush) 66
Thormbi (causes leg swellings) 66
Worms 66
The Romany Dog 66
Distemper 67
To Prevent Distemper 67
For Mange 67

Worm Prevention and Conditioner 67
For Poisoning 69
For Sore Pads 69
For Fleas and Ticks 69
Worming 69
Coat Conditioner 69
To Earn a Dog's Loyalty 71
The Romany Poacher 71
Bait For Catching Eels and Trout 71
Bait For Roach and Perch 71
For Bolting Rabbits From Their Holes 73
For Drawing Rabbits and Hares 73
to Your Fields 73
To Repel Rats and Mice 73
Chapter Seven   More Romany Lore 75
Chapter Eight   A Romany Larder 81
Kettle Broth 83
Trout With Bacon 83
Grilled Eel 84
Boiled Bacon Dinner 84
Fried Young Rabbit 85
Steamed Nettles 85
Pan Haggerty 86
Colcannon 86
Hedgerow Jelly 87
Chapter Nine   Some Romany Tales 89
Frosty 91
Orange and Lemon 95
Shadow Man 97
Chapter Ten   Oubliette 102
Appendix   A Romany Herbal 111
Select Biblography 115

Preface

Come the summer we'd borrow Old Ned and a sprung cart and Alesandro at the reins would stir up the dust on the Gisburn road. When I was a boy, Gipsy encampments were a common sight in the wilds of Lancashire and no outing was complete without a visit for pegs, lucky charms and a selection of cure-alls. My fascination with these people, with whom I had a tenuous link, has remained with me all of my life. Always interested in alternative lifestyles and alternative medicine, I started collecting Romany lore and remedies.

Many people are attracted to the falsely romantic image that some writers have given Gipsies. With association, this image rapidly disappears and takes all interest with it. Some people retain their interest and this takes a number forms. These forms include historical, linguistic and genealogical studies. Some collect folk tables or music or customs or vocabularies. Still others are merely content in knowing a loveable people. It is to the latter group that I most belong but this tapestry has picked up the other threads as well.

What I have written down here has grown out of a life-time's association and much of it is written from a personal point of view. I never intended to write an authoritative or academic book. I have tried to put down a comfortable, commonplace fireside book with something of interest to almost everyone in it.

On the personal level, it was intended to be cathartic as well but time has blunted my needle and faded the threads. Some of these pictures are now merely shadows on a wall and what remedies I have for life's disappointments and pains may only be sweet waters from a foul well. This is also in many respects an intensely personal book based on many intensely personal experiences so I beg forgiveness for its shortcomings.

Chapter One

Lifting the Latch

"When I gets married, I want a house with a number on the door, same as everyone else." (A young Gipsy)

The carrier arrived the day before we did. Mrs Ridgeway had the packing cases set down in the front room of the cottage amidst the few bare items that fulfilled the description "semi-furnished".

It was a subject for endless discussion between Pip and I that our entire childhood seemed to have been spent in the company of various " Mrs".

These ladies apparently never acquired a Mister along the way. Mrs Ridgeway was one of these. Mrs Nelson, who kept house for our maternal grandfather, was another.

Mother, Pip and I, having ceased wandering with a father who had a love of long distance, arrived at Burnley station on a rainy Tuesday evening with a further journey of six miles to go. Apart from a small, brown leather valise and an umbrella, mother had all of our belongings sent by the carrier.

It was getting dark and the wet streets were deserted. Our journey had been timed so that our arrival at Burnley coincided with the last bus to Sabden. Sure enough, the rusting green body of that conveyance rounded a corner and creaked to halt outside the station entrance.

Mother paid the driver and we all sat behind him so as not to miss his command to alight. Mother sat forward anxiously and peered out of the windscreen. The journey seemed endless. The black clouds on Pendle Hill and the misty drizzle veiled the darkening countryside for all but a few yards down the rutted lanes. If our rickety bus had ever been equipped with suspension coils, they no longer spared us the bone shaking bumps we had to take.

Mother sat forward in her seat and leaned over the driver's shoulder. "I do beg your pardon, driver, but this bus does stop at Sabden, doesn't it?"

To her surprise, the driver answered her in a broad Scots accent. "Aye mam, this bus do stop ae Sabden." Reassured, mother settled back on the seat between Pip and I.

It was quite dark as we climbed the heights above Padiham but faint twinkles picked out the lights of distant hamlets and the charcoal grey mills closed behind us.

Mother edged forward in her seat again and, in a tone that was almost confidential, asked the driver; "this bus will stop at Sabden, won' t it?"

"Aye mam", the driver grunted, "I'll set ye doon ae Sabden".

Reassured again, mother settled back into the seat. Pip nodded sleepily and I yawned several times. A strong wind boiled up and the rain lashed the windows and roof of the bus.

Mother leaned forward again. "Driver, we will stop at Sabden, won't we?"

In exasperation, the driver turned to mother and snapped, "mam, if this bus dunna stop ae Sabden, ye'll get the most damnable dunt ye've ever had i' yer life!".

Mother slumped back into the seat with a look akin to shellshock on her face. She was easily defeated and it took enormous courage for her to sally forth from her shell again. She did finally pluck up the courage to address the driver once more. She asked him if he knew how to get to our cottage.

"Aye," the driver replied, "ye canna miss it. Ye see, there's this cottage and, then, there's Sabden Brook!" As he said this, it sounded like the crack of doom. He made up for his earlier abruptness by putting us down at the bottom of the lane that followed Sabden Brook to our cottage gate.

As we descended the steps to the muddy ground, mother thanked him and said, "you are not from around these parts, are you?"

"Nae mam," was his response, "I'm frae Aberdeen."He smiled down on us benignly, shut the door and clattered back down the steep road to Burnley.

Mother extracted a small torch from her valise with which to light our way to the garden path. Herding us forward she pushed the picket gate half-open and it fell off its hinges. Mother laughed.

"Mummy," I inquired, "why are you laughing?"

"My darling", she smiled from tear streaked cheeks, "that's how I register despair."

From her raincoat pocket, mother extracted a large and heavy key, which she pushed into the lock of the ledge and brace door and turned it. She lifted the latch and we walked into a large, low beamed room that was cluttered with our packing cases and bits of furniture. Mother shone the torch around.

"I wonder if Mrs Ridgeway has left us some tea? I did ask for something in that order."

Presently, she noticed a light shining under a door at the back of the room. Beyond the door was a small, basic kitchen. To one side of it lay the scullery and to the other side, a pantry. A back door let out to a small yard with water closet, washhouse and woodshed. Beyond that lay a small overgrown garden and a couple of apple trees of the Ribstone Pippin variety.

The kitchen was warm and cosy. A woodburning stove gave off a faintly red glow. On the table stood a large meat and vegetable pie, more vegetables and gravy than meat. Meat was still rationed and what meat there was in the pie was quite unidentifiable.

Plates, utensils, cups and saucers had been neatly arranged on a polished cotton check tablecloth. A large oil lamp burned in the centre of the table. On the stove was a large kettle of boiling water and, perched on the black-leaded edge, was a teapot of the Brown Betty variety.

Outside the window, Old Mother Demdike was casting a storm spell. An inky brew of rain and hail beat frantically at the leaded panes.

Ridgey

J
MH-

Pip was sullen and we were all too tired to eat. Mother covered the pie and placed it on the pantry shelf.

While Pip and I sipped our warm, sweet, milky tea, mother slipped into the sitting room with her torch and unpacked some sheets, pillows and blankets. She climbed the open wooden stairs that led directly up to a large landing bedroom.

Having made up the bed and laid out our nightshirts, mother escorted us to the watercloset then filled a basin from the kettle. With a wet facecloth she mopped us down and led the way with the oil lamp.

For most of our childhood, Pip and I shared a large double bed. No matter where we started off, the sinking feather mattress rolled us together. Storms and eerie tales of broomstick rides to Hoarstones sent us flying into mother's bed.

The scent of my mother is as clear and clean on my nostrils now as it was then. It was the smell of lavender soap and perfumed talc sent to her in regular parcels by our nan.

Mother always slept in pink or cream satin slips of which she had quite a few left over from the affluent days before the war. These were carefully cleaned and cared for and folded neatly between sheets of tissue paper in her chest of drawers. When some part of the fabric became worn, it was stretched on her embroidery hoop and covered in silken birds and flowers. The necklines were trimmed in ribbons or old bits of lace that she had carefully hoarded for years. She shortened her Italian lace wedding gown and dyed it black. Its matching mantilla became a cushion cover.

The morning brought Pip and I a breakfast of cold meat and vegetable pie and warm, sweet, milky tea. While we sat at the kitchen table, mother started unpacking.

The cottage was a fairly wide though not deep two-storied affair. It was built in the soot begrimed local brown-grey stone, had a slate roof and stone-mullioned windows with small leaded panes. There was a pocket handkerchief of a front garden screened from the lane by a box hedge and a white picket fence. With the garden gate we had already become acquainted. It was to hang there, half off its hinges, like a derisive question mark, until Alesandro, a Spanish Gipsy journeying to Westmorland (now part of Cumbria) for the Appleby Horse Fair, stopped with us one summer and repaired it. To the other side of the lane the land dipped into Sabden Brook.

The cottage was damp and hard to heat in the winter. It was hot and airless in the summer. The ceilings were low and beamed and the walls were of plain painted plaster. There was a fireplace in the sitting room and another in the bedroom above it. Eider downs over handmade patchwork quilts helped to stave off the bite of winter.

Theoretically, the cottage was semi-furnished. To the few humble pieces there were added the furniture our parents had acquired from relatives or bought second hand and placed in storage during the four years before I came along. The only really distinguished item was a straight-backed Chippendale chair that was placed in a corner by the sitting room fire and dragged forward for mother's seances. Two olegraphs of Swiss lake scenes, a large plaster wall-hanging of Balmoral Castle and a faded sepia photograph of a Romany family group gathered beside their vardo broke the pale pink plaster monotony of the walls. A large engraving of an ancestral divine with whom we shared no religious sympathy hung on the stair wall.

As time went by, a number of framed needlework pieces were added to these. There was my mother's ATS emblem worked in silks, a schooner in full-rigging on a field of turgid blues, and East Anglian fishing village and a woodland scene in the Gipsy hot colours of a summer's day. An armchair and sofa had been acquired second hand and for these mother had made floral print covers to match the chintz curtains. At one end of the mantelpiece on a hand of gnarled yew stood mother's crystal ball (it had been her mother's before her) and on the other end stood a lotus blossom painted wooden ankh, the larger version of the little silver ones that hung around our necks.

From my mother, I acquired a certain indifference to food beyond the purpose of sustenance. We ate well enough one day in each week when Mrs Ridgeway came in to help our mother do, but not beyond the basic Romany cuisine.

Mrs Ridgeway was a 'broad' big-boned Lancashire woman whose affection for us was demonstrated by a crushing hug that drew our suffocating faces deep into her ample cleavage. There our tossled heads of hair tangled in her Spanish shawl and silver coin necklace. Mother once remarked that we had not been brought up on the breast to which Ridgey (that's what we called her) responded, "Aye, but they be a makin up for it now, mam!"

Mother filled our world and we filled hers. Had it not been for us, mother would have been a lonely woman. She was regarded with suspicious awe by most of the village women and was seldom able to cultivate the close friendships that many women need. She kept in touch with a few girlfriends from her schooldays and from her stint in the ATS. She was a voluminous letter writer but had a completely Victorian contempt for the niceties of punctuation. She would only use dots and dashes to separate one idea from another. For the most part, her spelling rested on an idiosyncratic use of phonetics. Why was the "P" necessary in psychology - you didn't hear it! To a limited extent, I inherited her disdain for the superfluous.

Though Pip and I were not equipped with the necessary criteria to judge such things, we had it on good authority that our mother was beautiful. And even when our circumstances were very reduced, mother had style. Pip inherited our father's swarthiness but I was gorgio fair like my mother. As a child, my hair was ash blonde and I had deep blue eyes. A Morrocan Gipsy asked my father if I was for sale. I wasn't but my father received an ornately engraved, ivory handled dagger in exchange for a lock of my hair. Apparently, the Gipsy seemed to regard this as some sort of a charm.

When we had any money, mother could be extravagantly impractical. A picture book or a box of coloured pencils or paints and a bottle of Eau de toilette headed the shopping list. Oddly enough, these purchases, carefully nurtured in their brown wrappings all the way home, worked a wonderful psychology and made the evening's bland faire taste sinfully good. Mother would smile as we unwrapped our booty, "thought we' d just pretend we are dining at Simpson's in the Strand."

On nice afternoons, mother would meet us from school. Before she collected us, mother would spend a couple of hours sitting in the sun on a bench on the village green. She would do her knitting and have her tea from an old tartan flask carried about in a brown paper bag.

Our kitchen drawers were filled with brown paper bags, wrapping paper, string, parcel tape and an assortment of nails, screws and bits of wire found lying about and surreptitiously and self-consciously gathered up. "It might come in useful someday." And, indeed, most things did come in useful. Nothing was thrown away.

We didn't have such nice teas as some of our school friends had. There were wedges of bread and margarine and a pot of Ridgey's homemade jam. It was years before Pip and I realised that a spread of margarine on a digestive biscuit was not a euphemism for an ice-cream wafer. Although mother had some money of her own and our grandfather continued to send us money to help us get by and pay Ridgey, ours was a genteel poverty made golden by the dignity of our mother who met each of life's disappointments with the stoical bearing of her ancestors.

Lunch was usually a pan of Cross and Blackwell's condensed mushroom soup made with water rather than milk. I would carefully spoon up the watery stock and move the tiny cubes of mushroom to the side of the dish. Then, when a neat little pile of brown and grey was all that was left, I would scoop it up and eat it with considerable relish.

"Why do you do that, Jem," Pip asked.

"I like to save the best bits for last," I smiled. But then, I've been putting the brown and grey bits on the side for most of my life and the best of them are illusory.

Most evenings we did not have meat for dinner. It was still rationed anyway and our coupons were saved up to provide a small roast that appeared at the table some Sundays. We had rabbit and fish when our father paid one of his extended visits. Sometimes there was a bit of liver, which mother convinced us was steak, from the butcher. When it could be had, offal was the cheapest meat that could be bought. For years though our schoolmates wondered how we could afford to have steak so often, which could only have been had on the black market anyway. At other times, mother would come home from the butcher's with a large ham bone for a dog that, at the time, we didn't have. This still had some bits of meat clinging to it and was boiled up with soak peas to make a thick and tasty soup.

The rabbits our father shot or snared were salted to keep and used in pies and stews. The frequency with which we were fed this meat put me off rabbit for much of my adult life. We had fresh fish on Fridays when our father was around or when I was old enough and experienced enough to catch and clean them myself. Our father was a lapsed Catholic but fish on Friday was still a tradition that was adhered to. When there was no fish, we ate scrambled eggs made with powdered eggs, that part of the chicken having failed to pass muster as meat.

I can still see the tradesmen and working men doff their cloth caps as mother walked down the high street with her wicker basket over one arm. She seemed to be benignly oblivious to these little attentions as she vaguely counted the coins in her hand and bit her lip in thoughtful budgeting. Unlike most of the villagers, mother took nothing on credit and I think that she was respected by the shopkeepers for this. Many were the times that an extra slice of liver or a sausage from the butcher or an extra pound of potatoes or carrots from the greengrocer were found in the brown parcels when they were unwrapped on the kitchen table. At such times she had an aristocratic disdain for the words "thank you." To have said it would have been to acknowledge the need. It would have humiliated her and embarrassed the shopkeeper. To mother, such things were unsolicited gifts. Charity was neither asked for nor accepted.

Mother always took the optimistic view that "something would turn up" in life. Something was always going to turn up. "Never mind dear, something will turn up," she would smile her sad smile. But nothing ever did turn up, which is probably why I became a cynic. If anything was unpleasant for her, she merely pretended that it didn't exist.

She had one trait that drove Pip and I to distraction and that was selective deafness. She heard only what she wanted to hear. We could put our case to her with logic and succinctness, forcefully argued and laid before her with all of the ability of a barrister pleading his case. Mother would listen, nod in agreement, smile her sad smile and return with stubborn directness to her own view because ours had no relevance to what she deemed the well-ordered running of her world. In later years, her long overdrawn account with reality only turned the dividends of defeat and a stoical resignation.

A natural ability with animals was a gift that our mother communicated to us. This gift was proscribed in her by the limitation of her fears. The whole of Aten's creation offered no fears at all for me, always allowing for the single exception of humankind. No animal has ever hurt me. Consequently, I much prefer their company to that of people.

Our childhood was one long cottage hospital with Pip and I bringing every injured bird and wounded animal we stumbled across into our kitchen. These our mother nursed back to health and then persuaded us to tearfully release them back into the wild. What mother lacked in sound medical knowledge she made up for with a fund of ancient home remedies (many of them used on us) and her gentle and calming influence.

Miraculously, I don't recall her ever losing a patient. Some really quite hopeless cases were brought back from the brink or so it seemed to us. She taught us how to hold birds and feed them with an eye dropper filled with egg yolk.

Our hair was cut round a pudding basin and, unless at school, we went barefoot or in clogs in the summer so as not to wear out our decent shoes. We wore dark blue corduroy knicker-bockers and red check shirts and I had a canary yellow neckerchief of which I was very proud.

We made our own entertainment apart from the radio, which we huddled around on Sunday evenings for a play. We kept scrapbooks that mother made up for us from sheets of brown wrapping paper bound together in sewn cardboard covers. With a paste made from flour and water we stuck into these pictures we liked of animals and birds that we cut from the magazines that nanna sent to mother. We collected flowers and leaves on our rambles over the hill and into Bowland. There was fostered in us then a love of the natural world and a sense of the wonder of Aten's creation. We cut and painted cardboard boxes into castles and farms and villages. The paints were primary powdered colours of red, blue and yellow kept in large jars in the sideboard. These were mixed with water in old tins and mother taught us how to make a whole range of different colours by blending the right amounts of the primaries together.

We loved a good ghost story but tales of the boggart that haunted the troughs in the sides of the hill sent us running straight into mother's bed again at night. We told stories and recited verse and read aloud to each other. Mother had a couple of poems published and I started to write poetry as well.

On a frosty, coming of winter November afternoon, I came home from school to find mother kneeling before the sittingroom fire. On the hearth a pile of papers burned and on her lap was a yellowed shoebox. From this she took folded bits of paper, opened them, read them and put them on the fire.

"But mummy, these are your poems," I protested as I handled a couple of sheets. "Why are you burning them?"

Mother looked at me wistfully and sighed, "you see, I was very young and very much in love and didn't know any better."

I watched the paper glow, the letters lift up, the cinders drift in the chimney's updraft and the embers settle back on the hearth to glint like fireflies in the twilight and die.

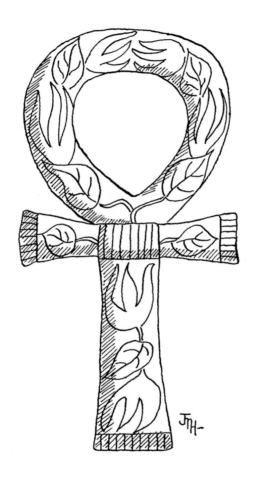

Chapter Two

A Romany History and a Short One

The European Gipsy word for men of their own race is *Rom* (hence Romanies). The Armenian word is *Lom* and the Persian is *Dom*. These have been seen to be phonetically correspondent to the Sanskrit "*Doma*" and the present day Indian word Dom which means a man of low caste who earns his living by dancing and singing. The Dom's of the west and north-west provinces of India have many features in common with the Gipsies.

Other than the Jews, there is no race so widely distributed in the world as the Gipsies - a Diaspora that might even be as old as the Jewish one. However, the race is not the same everywhere. A clear distinction can be drawn between Oriental and Occidental Gipsies. But whether wanderers or sedentary they have successfully retained their characteristics in the face of extraordinary periodic hostility.

A small drop of Romany blood is enough to colour one's whole life. The Earl of Birkenhead who became Lord Chancellor in 1919 is an excellent example of this. In temperament, he was more Romany than Gorgio.

It is rare to meet anyone who has Romany blood who is not prepared to proudly admit it.

Generations of Romanies have handed on a fierce independence and extraordinary vigour and yet, very few people know much about them and many Romanies know very little about themselves. Who are the Romanies and where did they come from? Various explanations for the origin of the Romanies have been set down. They are Egyptians or the Sintians of Homer or the Signnae of Herodotus or Sudras expelled by Tamerlane.

It has long been recognised that the answer to the problem lies in the Romany language. In 1763, Stefan Valyi, a Hungarian theological student in Leyden showed that the language was Indian of Aryan origin related to the original Sanskrit. It was not until 1844 with the publication of further research that the linguistic answer became widely known and an investigation of the Indian origin of Gipsies was seriously undertaken.

The uniform agreement among philologists in assigning the birthplace of the Romany language to India is, however, a different matter from establishing the exact locality of the Race's origin. The Romany language is indisputably of Indian origin but we cannot refer it to any dialect past or present. It has been suggested that they were even wanderers in their homeland. At all events, they are a very ancient people and it has been suggested that their origins reach right back into prehistoric times.

There are various ancient texts that suggest that there was a Gipsy presence outside of India long before AD 1000. The poet Firdusi refers to Gipsies in his Shâh Nâme and says that they were present in Persia around AD 420. Chronicles of the 7th Century tell us that these moved on to settle in Arabia. By the 9th Century, this group became so great a nuisance in the lower Tigris valley that many of them were transported to the northern frontier of Syria. In AD 855 many more were carried off as prisoners into the Greek Empire.

The generally accepted date for the appearance of the Gipsies in Europe is AD 1417. However, we have the references placing them in south-eastern Europe from at least AD 855. We also know that they were in Corfu by the early 14th Century and their presence there made contact with the Italians inevitable.

It is fairly certain that Gipsies were present in the Peloponnesus for a long while. A number of ruins there are called Gyphtokastron, which means "Gipsy Fortress."

A charter granted by Mircen I, Prince of Wallachia, in AD 1387 indicated that Romanian Gipsies had been serfs since at least AD 1370. Some authorities accept that the Bemische recorded at Frankfurt-am-Main in AD 1495 were Gipsies and Gipsy settlements at Hildesheim in AD 1407, Basle AD 1414 and Messen in AD 1416 were an established fact.

What is fairly certain in philological studies is that the Romany language cannot have evolved much before AD 1000. Some early references may be to wandering tinkers who were itinerant fortune-tellers and horse-dealers. We do know that those people who are recorded as having arrived in AD 1417 would not have created such a stir had they not been new and different. After AD 1417 we have many accounts of Romany journeys across Europe. There are numerous references in municipal accounts of gifts made to this or that duke, earl or count of Little Egypt and his followers.

From about 1438 onwards Gipsies spread rapidly through every country in Europe. The accounts of two chroniclers at Lubeck numbered one band at 300. At their head rode a duke and a count in rich apparel and leading hunting dogs. They bore letters of safe conduct from, among others, the Emperor Sigismund. It was said that they were doing penance in a seven-year pilgrimage for infidelity to the Christian faith. In parts of Europe they were variously labelled as charlatans, thieves and horse-thieves.

It is not known when the Romanies first entered Britain. They are first mentioned by the name of Gipsies in the accounts of the Lord High Treasurer for Scotland in 1505. This reference is to a new incursion and indicates that they were in this country before that date. James II of Scotland enacted laws to put away "sorners, fancied fools, vagabonds, out-liers, masterful beggars, cairds and such like runners about".

In 1449 an Act of the Scottish Parliament was directed against "sorners, over-liers, and masterful beggars, with horse, hounds and other goods." When the word 'Egyptians'appears in the Scottish Acts of Parliament it is used to describe just these very people singled out in the 1449 Act. The king commanded the Lord High Treasurer to pay the "Egyptians" £7 in 1505. It is likely that this was a charity payment. The king was James IV and the change in royal attitude from the time of James II is remarkable. James IV and James V seem to have gone out of their way to aid the "Egyptians" financially and recommended them to the charity of the ruler of the next country on their itinerary.

In 1540, James V granted the Gipsies astonishing privileges. This was, in effect, a treaty between the king and John Faw, Lord and Earl of Little Egypt. Walter Simson offered the explanation that James V was gullible and had a fondness for Gipsies and was "led up the garden" by John Faw who was quite a personage at the Scottish court.

Simson's case was that the thievery and roguishness of the Gipsies had got so far out of hand that Faw was asked to quit Scotland. Scotland was profitable for Faw and his people so Faw concocted a tale of rebellion. Faw said he could not return to his own country without all of his tribe with him. He needed help to round them up and the provision of ships in order to depart. But the rebellion had been a put-up job and any such real threat would have been speedily settled by Faw. A dispute that went on for many years did erupt later between the Baillies and the Faas over the right to the Gipsy Crown but this was not an outcome of the ' rebellion.'

The treaty that granted the Romanies the right to practice their own customs and laws in Scotland was soon reversed. The decree of banishment did not effectively rid Scotland of the Gipsies but it does seem to have driven the Faws south of the border because they turn up in Durham in 1549.

In England, the Gipsies are first mentioned in *A Dyalog of Syr Thomas More, Knyght*. A witness questioned in the death of one Richard Hunne is an "Egyptian" woman who could foretell marvellous things by reading the palm. Hale's Chronicles mention two ladies of the court dressing "like the Egyptians" in 1517. The name appears again in John Skelton's (Poet Laureate to Henry VIII) *Elynoure Rumminge*. The word "Gipsy" appears for the first time in Skelton's *Garland of Laurel* published in 1526 in the line: "By Mary Gipsy, quod scripsi scripsi."

In 1612, Samuel Reid published his *Art of Juggling* and an English Gipsy's name is mentioned for the first time. Reid says the Egyptians invaded England in 1528 and earned a living from fortune-telling, palm-reading and cheating. Their king was Giles Hather and Kit Calot was his queen. In terms of population, Holinshed's Chronicle states that "they are now supposed, of one sex or another, to amount to above ten thousand persons."

An Act of Parliament was passed in England in 1530 to repress "many outlandyeshe People callynge themselfes Egyptians" and to stop further immigration. By this Act, apprehended Gipsies forfeited all their goods and were forced to leave the country within fifteen days or be imprisoned. The Act had little effect and does not seem to have been unduly enforced.

In 1544, a tribe of Gipsies was apprehended in Huntingdonshire and deported to the Continent and another group in Lincolnshire was sent to Norway. But for the most part, Romanies travelled the country without molestation. It was not unusual for Englishmen to consort with Gipsies as legislation against this indicates. Men and women were hanged for it.

The last time that the death penalty was enacted against a Gipsy (for being a Gipsy) was at the end of Cromwell's Proctectorate when thirteen were hanged at the Suffolk assizes. However, repressive legislation was still being enacted as late as 1908.

Deportation remained a common form of repression for a long time. Gipsies were banished to the Americas in 1665 and 1715. There are many thousands of Romanies in the United States now. Other European countries adopted this method of repression.

In Ireland, the word "Tinker" is most commonly used to describe travelling folk. Real Romanies have never invaded

Ireland in any great numbers so the word "Gipsy" has little currency.

While closely allied, the Irish Tinkers are quite distinct from the Gipsies and have a language of their own - Shelta. They have many of the same customs and follow the same way of life but they are a distinct race. The Shelta language has become an area of research all it own. It is spoken by certain Irish Tinker families in preference to Gaelic or English. Real Romanies do not like Tinkers even though Tinkers have no particular dislike of them. The dislike seems to stem from the fact that Romanies were, and are, too often blamed for the sins of the Tinkers. However, there are occasional intermarriages.

By and large the Romanies are an uncompromising race. Theirs' is a free spirit even when forced to lead a sedentary existence. It is their freedom and the call of the open road that appeals to the romantic side of many of us. The history of the Romanies is one long journey, seemingly without purpose sometimes other than to be on the move.

". . . and there," said Alesandro, "the only way to learn about life is to live it and the best remedy for being sad is to learn something."

Chapter Three

Some Romany Customs and Lore

When Romany families first began to arrive in Britain they called themselves the "Dukes of Little Egypt," hence the name "Gipsies".

Early references to the Romanies called them "Minions of the Moon". In paganism, the Moon is sacred to and an outward manifestation of the Goddess.

Romanies stood out from other people not just because of their way of life and appearance. They have long been known for their liberal attitudes and centuries ago Thomas Harman wrote "they take lechery for no sin, but natural fellowship and good liking love."

Gipsy magic and healing was strongly rooted in paganism. In the minds of the common people, the gipsies were associated with sorcery and witchcraft. But the very paganism that brought down the wrath of the Church on the gipsies was one of the reasons why ordinary people tolerated them and made use of the services they offered.

In Romany mythology, the Earth (De Develeski) is the Divine Mother. She is the supreme deity of the Gipsies and is regarded as more important than God, who only came into being when the Earth had already formed. This concept is strong among peoples who live an outdoor life close to nature.

A strong belief in the supernatural occupied a central role in Romany communities. Evil spirits were believed to constantly roam the night in search of victims. Charms against these included four-leafed clovers, the breast bones of kingfishers and jays and small holed stones. The 'Evil Eye' was greatly feared. Talismans of bead-like fossils called ' adderstones' were worn to ward off the Evil Eye. Bad omens included dreams of snakes or blood, dogs howling, meeting a donkey, a funeral or a squint-eyed woman on the open road. Good luck was associated with the moon (symbol of the Goddess), falling stars, white horses, little green frogs and pieces of coral. Precious stones were worn with the wearer's sign of the zodiac. Later Romany beliefs were influenced by Christian thinking. Myths about their origins incorporated Biblical imagery. One legend claims that the gipsies descended from the first murderer, Cain and were forever doomed to wander the Earth because of the terrible sin of their ancestor.

A lighter tale tells how o Del (God) made the first man out of chalk and baked him in an oven. o Del overcooked him and made the first negro. o Del took another man from the oven too soon and created the first white man. o Del made a third attempt and baked a man to a nice even brown - the first Gipsy.

Ghosts, demons and vampires all figure in Romany folklore. The Gipsies' favourite instrument, the violin, was said to be the Devil's creation. According to a legend, Mara, a beautiful Gipsy girl, fell in love with a gorgio (a non-Gipsy.) He did not, however, love her. Mara sold the

souls of her family to the Devil in return for his help. Her father became the sound-box, her four brothers became the strings and her mother became the bow. Mara learned to play it well and its enchanting sound made her gorgio fall in love with her. The Devil reappeared and carried them both off to Hell. The violin was left behind and found by a poor Gipsy boy.

Romany marriage rites are the simplest imaginable - often no more than a joining of hand before witnesses. In this, there is an extraordinary continuity with the Pagan hand-fasting. The validity of these marriages has been upheld by English courts.

A Gipsy girl shows her favour toward a man by throwing a coin-filled cake over a hedge to him. If a man wears two red handkerchiefs on his jacket and a girl takes one, the couple are betrothed. Marriage ceremonies varied between communities. In one, the couple jump a broom together. In another, the couple clasp hands while bread and salt are sprinkled over them. In Wales, couples jumped over a besom made of flowering broom.

Another pledge involved the halving of a load of bread. From pricked fingers, the groom smears his blood on one half and the bride on the other. The bride eats from his half and he from hers. Drinking from the same cup also cemented a relationship. Bread baked from flour moistened with wine and stirred with a ram's horn then eaten by the couple also constituted a marriage. Basque Gipsies venerate the ram's horn and, in this, we see the survival of the worship of Cernunnos, the horned god.

"Regardin' a piece of paper," Alesandro observed, "It's what we says to one another that really matters."

Gipsy rites were followed by a civil ceremony and a feast which often lasted for days. Divorce was affected by a couple shaking hands over the carcase of a dead animal.

For a month and a day after giving birth, Romany women were held to be unclean. The bed on which the baby was born was burnt. The mother was not allowed to cook or touch any food but her own. She slept apart and ate apart from others during this time and her husband was not allowed to touch his child until after the christening.

A race without taboos is a race without virility. Many Romanies today are not so concerned with taboos as were their forefathers. Most of their traditional taboos were associated with women, food and death and the vast majority of these with women. Until the later third of the last century, English Gipsies observed a great many taboos associated with women. The knowledge of these taboos is still current even if unobserved.

The Romany word for unclean is "*mochardi*" But this has nothing to do with dirtiness. It is an aspect of ancient religion. Unclean in the ceremonial sense and, therefore, a spiritual pollution. Women, even in good health, were once regarded as mochardi because they were a source of pollution to the health and strength of a man.

A man would not eat or drink anything a woman stepped over nor touch any plate cup or utensil a woman stepped over. At the extreme a Romany man would refuse to drink tap water because the pipes ran underground and a woman must, therefore, step over them. This is a very old taboo. In Ancient Greece women were prohibited fron crossing a running stream at the time of menstruation. As far as food and utensils were concerned, this taboo was extended to men by some Romanies. Food in which a hair was found was mochardi and thrown away.

Among some Gipsy groups, a woman was not allowed to let her hair down or to comb it out in front of a man. This applied even if the man were her husband.

The way in which women sat was once regulated. Unmarried girls sat with their legs crossed and their feet tucked underneath them. Married women could sit with legs extended as long as they did not separate them. In the presence of men, women had to keep their legs pressed tightly together. This prohibition applied even if the man present was husband, father or brother.

Another taboo that was widespread was that a woman must never pass in front of a seated man, she must pass behind him.

Menstruating women and very young babies were regarded as mochardi but children of either sex were not subject to taboos and not accounted susceptible to defilement.

A woman's clothing must not be washed with a man's. At the extreme, among some Gipsies, a woman's clothing could not even be hung out to dry with a man's and under no circumstances should a man touch them. No such distinction was made for the clothing of children who were regarded as neuter until the onset of puberty. A male child became defilable between the ages of ten and thirteen and a female became subject to taboos with the onset of her first period. Among the purer-blooded Romanies today there are still more taboos that are still observed associated with menstruation than anything else.

The Boswells from whom T.W. Thompson obtained most of his knowledge of Romany lifeways were very reticent about speaking of all sexual matters. Many Romanies are and there appears to be an almost cultural prudishness despite the once observed reputation they had for liberal attitudes. Interest appears to have been more in the observance than in the theory. Views concerning any departure from the sexual norm would seem to be regarded as a personal matter. I have met a number of Romany men who apparantly inclined towards bisexuality.

Once while still very young and golden-haired, I travelled with a Basque Romany family. For a while, I was very much drawn into the family circle and made to feel a part of it. As I sat with Sancho by the campfire before daylight's gate he offered me the company of his wife. When I politely declined, he offered to sleep with me himself. An invitation that I also politely declined. There only ever was one Romany man for whom my bond of friendship was so intense that I would have considered this an option. Just as there only ever was one Romany girl from whom I snatched a kiss one summer's day in the Trough of Bowland.

Inter-marriage was once very common in Romany families although brother-sister couplings were prohibited. Romany tribes are often very extended families - ties of blood are very strong and very important.

Trial marriages were not unknown. However, few Romany women appear to marry more than once. Prostitution is most uncommon. By and large, Romany girls are modest and chaste although verbal chastity would pass unnoticed.

A strongly Catholic prohibition of pre-nuptial sex may account, as it does in those strongly Catholic countries, for the intense male bonding that often occurs among Romany men.

Infidelity in a woman was once severely punished by Romanies in this country and, generally, Romanies had high moral standards. But Romany attitudes have changed with time just as Gorgio ones have.

The dying were removed from their caravans to pass away out of doors. Many Romanies were buried with their most valuable possessions, coins and lucky charms to ensure a comfortable afterlife. Some gipsies still burn the dead person's caravan so that his spirit will not come back to haunt it as a vampire.

Romany children became active members of their community almost as soon as they could walk. In olden times, Romany children acquired the art of riding very early in life.

Much of Romany beliefs tied up with the old nature religions and they observe some relics of tree-worship.

The festival of Green George (the Green Man, Jack in the Green) is the chief celebration of spring for many Romanies. Some keep it on Easter Monday and others on St. George's Day (23 April.). On the day before the festival a young willow tree is cut down, decorated with garlands and leaves and placed in the ground similar to the Maypole. Pregnant women place one of their garments under the tree and leave it overnight. If in the morning they find a leaf of the tree lying on the garment, they can be assured of an easy delivery. The old and sick go to the tree in the evening, spit on it three times and say "you will soon die, but let us live". The next morning, the Romanies gather round the willow. Central to the festival is Green George, a youth or boy who is completely clothed from head to toe in green leaves and blossoms. Green George throws handfuls of grass to the tribal livestock so that they do not lack for fodder throughout the year. Then

Green George takes up three iron nails, which have been soaked in water for three days and nights, and hammers them into the willow. He then pulls them out and throws them into a stream to propitiate the water spirits. The final part of the ritual is a pretence of throwing Green George into the water (in fact, only a mannikin made of branches and leaves is ducked.)

All chant;

> Green George, we bring,
> Green George we accompany,
> May he feed our herds well.
> If not, to the water with him.

The power to heal is clearly ascribed to the willow while Green George himself, the human double of the tree, is a symbol of fertility.

On the eve of Easter Sunday, Romanies used to take a wooden container like a band box resting cradle-wise on two cross pieces of wood. They placed herbs and simples in this together with the dried carcass of a lizard or snake that everyone had first touched with their fingers. The container was then wrapped in red and white wool. Then it was carried by the oldest man from tent to tent. Every member of the band spat into it once and the tribe's sorceress uttered some spells over it. Finally, it was thrown into running water. The Romanies believed that by performing this ceremony they dispelled all the illnesses that would otherwise have afflicted them in the course of the year. Similar forms of "scapegoat" magic are practiced in a great many pagan societies.

Romany men were as concerned with their personal appearance and adornment as were the women. They were normally excellent judges of horse flesh and excellent animal trainers. They could nurse great enmity towards those who had given them or theirs offence but they also cultivated strong friendships with each other. Elements in the Romany language give us a glimpse of their attitude to life. The word "*merripen*" stands both for life and death and, according to George Borrow, they had no word for glory.

Chapter Four

Romany Remedies

There was a time when Romanies would rarely have called in a doctor. For ordinary ailments and illness, they still rely on their own medicinal knowledge.

In common with many peoples who live close to nature, the Romanies kept a store of medicinal plants and herbs. Once, it was not at all unusual to see bunches of plants and herbs hanging to dry on the sides of Gipsy vardos. Leaves, flowers, roots and barks were dried and packed in envelopes and jars, labelled and ready for any emergency. This is less common now and many Romanies have forgotten the formulas of their traditional remedies or just neglected their use in favour of modern conventional medical treatments.

Many plants and herbs were collected in country lanes and on river banks and were regarded by the Romanies as far more valuable than most of the plants one takes a lot of trouble to grow. The common nettle that is freely available has a real price on it when purchased from a herbalist. For many years proprietary medicines used similar plants and formulas to those used in Romany remedies.

The common stinging nettle was used by Romanies for blood pressure - in common with spinach, it contains all of the necessary chlorophyll for softening hardened arteries.

One cardinal remedy used by the Gipsies was Romany Balm, a very ancient remedy that was said to scarcely ever fail to cure skin complaints.

Before the invention of Penicillin, Romanies used to keep a jam pot on which mould was cultured. This was scraped off and used to dress wounds and sores with great effect. Spider webs culture Penicillin and, for centuries, Romanies placed the web over cuts and wounds. The fine, sticky lattice of the web also aided coagulation.

Well into this century, medicinal concoctions were sold door to door by Romanies. There are fewer wise men and women around now, so I have preserved these remedies.

A Note on Romany Measures

Doses are given in measures of a wineglass. This is the standard wineglass with a capacity of one-sixteenth of a pint.

Dr = Dram (Drachm) - A unit of weight one-sixteenth of an ounce avoirdupois. Before 1864 it also formed the eighth part of one ounce apothecary's weight.

Many Romany practitioners adhered to the "old" ways and used the apothecary's weights.

A pint preparation generally produces 14 to 16 wineglassfuls - a week's treatment.

Asthma and Other Chest Complaints

Boil one ounce of leaves of the Sweet Chestnut Tree (*Castaneasativa*) to every one and a half pints of water for ten minutes. Strain and cool. Add half an ounce of honey and half an ounce of glycerine. Drink a small wineglassful first thing in the morning and again after the last meal of the day.

Baldness

Mix thoroughly two ounces of pure unsalted Hog lard with a dram of Chrysorobin. Rub the resulting ointment into the scalp.

Balm (Romany Balm)

This is what is famously known as Romany Balm and was believed to be the invention of the Albanian and Romanies Zingari.

Place four ounces of the fat from pig's kidneys with one ounce of cuttings from the 'Frog' of the horse hoof (horse-hoof clippings), one Houseleek (a rosette-shaped plant) and one ounce of bark scrapings from the Elder Tree into an enamelled pan over a slow heat. Stir while the fat is sizzling. Simmer for half an hour then strain into a clean jar. Use this ointment on any sores, cuts, boils, bruises and skin complaints.

Beauty Ointment (Face Cream)

Melt together over a gentle heat two and a half ounces of Spermaceti, one half pint of Almond Oil, one half ounce of prepared Calamine. Strain through a fine sieve, rubbing it through. Store in airtight jars. Use freely at night and sparingly during the day as a base for face-powder. This was used the world over by Romany chis.

Beauty Cream (Called Gipsy Beauty Cream)

Place two ounces of pure unsalted Pork lard in an earthen jar with one ounce of chopped Red Dock Root and two ounces of Elder flowers. Heat for one hour and strain. Add two ounces of Cold Cream and blend together until cold. Store in an airtight jar. This is also a good remedy for blackheads.

Bladder Ailments

Boil one ounce of Parsley Piert (Alchemilla arvensis) in one pint of water for a minute. Strain and cool.

Drink a small wineglassful twice a day.

Blood Pressure

Boil one ounce of common Stinging Nettle (*Urtica dioica*) in one pint of water for five minutes. Strain and reboil the liquid before bottling. Drink a full small wineglass of this three times a day.

Boils and Skin Inflamations

Boil one ounce of Echinacea Root (Echinacea augustifolia) to each pint of water. Drink a full small wineglass of this twice a day and dab the affected area with the solution.

Melt together four ounces of coarse Resin powder, two ounces of Yellow Wax, eight ounces of Lard, one ounce of Almond Oil and one quarter ounce of Boric Powder over a gentle heat. Strain through a fine muslin and stir while it cools. Store in jars.

Apply to boils and cover with a linen bandage.

Catarrh

Dry some leaves of the Horse Chestnut Tree. Steep them in a solution of one ounce of salt petre to a quarter of a pint of warm water. Dry them again, rub into a powder and burn them on a tin plate and inhale the fumes before going to sleep.

Make a solution of one ounce of common rock salt to one pint of water and sniff a little of this up the nose in the morning.

Chest Complaints and Hacking Coughs

Boil one quarter ounce each of Mousear, Life Root, Liquorice Root, Golden Seal, Marshmallow Root and Iceland Moss with one half ounce of Linseed in one quarter pint of water for 20 minutes. Add two tablespoons of honey. Drink a small wineglassful three times a day.

The Romanies considered this one of the finest remedies known.

Blend four ounces of ordinary cheap grade Eau-de-Cologne with a quarter ounce of Formalin. Shake well and store in a tightly stoppered bottle. Rub a little between the palms of the hands and inhale deeply. A drop or two can be sprinkled on a handkerchief or a pillow without damage to the fabric.

Chilblains

Boil parsnips in two pints of unsalted water. Strain the liquid and mix in one tablespoon of powered alum. Stir well. Bathe the hands or feet in the solution for 20 minutes. Allow the solution to dry without rinsing. Continue to use the solution until the chilblains are gone.

Constipation

Boil one ounce of bark from the Alder Tree (*Prinos verticillatus*) in one pint of water for five minutes.

Drink a small wineglassful at night.

This is a very ancient Romany remedy and is very like Cascara (Californian Buckthorn - *Rhamnus purshiana*) which was used as a purgative.

Boil one ounce of Jalap Root and one pea-size piece of Aloes in one pint of water for ten minutes. Mash the root well to get all the juice out. Strain. Drink a small wineglassful morning and night.

Coughs

Place one quarter of a pint of vinegar and some finely broken up Liquorice in a basin. Put into a very hot oven and stir until Liquorice is completely dissolved. Add two ounces of honey and the juice of one whole lemon. Take one teaspoonful whenever troubled by the cough.

This is excellent for children.

Cystitis

Boil one ounce of Couch Grass Root (Agropyrum repens) in one and a half pints of water for five minutes. Strain.

Drink a small wineglassful five or six times a day.

Diarrhoea

Boil one ounce of Rhubarb Root in one pint of water for five minutes. Strain. A small dose of the liquid should be taken. A large dose will work as a safe laxative (*aparient*). This is a classic example of the homeopathic principle of treating like with like.

Infuse a tea of herb Agrimony using one ounce of the herb to one pint of boiling water.

Take a tablespoonful two or three times a day.

Foot Ointment (Gipsy Foot Ointment)
Melt together four ounces of tallow, one ounce of powdered Sulphur and one fluid ounce of Olive Oil. Stir well while cooling. Rub a little on the feet before a walk.

This ointment was used by the nomads of the Balkans whose mode of transport was walking and it is said that no corns will ever appear if this is used.

Gastritis
(This Remedy is called DECOCTUM QUERCUS)
Boil one ounce of Oak bark in one quart of water until the solution is the colour of whisky. Strain. Drink a wineglassful after each meal.

Gout
Boil one ounce of Woodwort (*Stachis palustri*), one ounce of powdered Rhubarb Root (*Rheum palmatum*) and one ounce of Willow Bark (*Salix alba*) in three pints of water for 15 minutes. Take two tablespoons morning and night. This is also good for Sciatica.

Hair Stimulant

Boil one ounce of Rosemary (*Rosemarinus officinalis*) in one pint of water for five minutes. Strain.

Rub the liquid into the scalp at night.

Headaches and Neuralgia

Boil one ounce of Ladies'Slipper root (Cypripedium pubesceno) in one pint of water for ten minutes. Strain and bottle.

Drink a wineglassful when attacks are on. This is also a good sleep-inducer.

Herb Beer

Take two ounces of Burdock leaves, one ounce of Yarrow, one ounce of Dandelion Herb, eight ounces of Malt, one ounce of Hops, two ounces of sugar and one ounce of yeast. Place all the ingredients except the sugar and yeast in a large pan with ten pints of water. Bring to a boil and simmer for two hours. Strain off the liquor into an earthenware or enamelled pan. When the liquor is just blood temperature stir in the sugar and the yeast (mix the yeast and sugar together with a little of the liquor before pouring into the bulk of the brew.) Let it stand in a warm place for 24 hours having placed a piece of cloth over the pan during this time. Skim off the yeast that has risen to the top and bottle the liquor, preferably in screw-top bottles. Leave to stand for a further two days and the brew will be ready to drink.

The Romanies also regarded this as a fortifying tonic.

Hoarseness

Boil one ounce of Black Currant leaves in one pint of water. Strain and bottle.

Take one tablespoonful two or three times a day.

Horehound and Wormwood Tonic Beer

Boil together one ounce of Horehound, one ounce of Wormwood, one ounce of Hops, and eight ounces of Malt in ten pints of water. Once the liquor has been brought to the boil, simmer for two hours. Strain the liquor through muslin into a large earthenware vessel or enamelled pan. Mix two ounces of Brown Sugar and one ounce of yeast with a little of the cooled (to blood temperature) liquid. Stir this into the bulk of the liquid. Cover with a cloth and let stand in a warm place for 24 hours. Skim off the yeast that has risen to the top and bottle.

Indigestion

Boil one ounce of Mandrake Root (*Podophyllum peltatum*) in one pint of water for five minutes. Strain. Take one teaspoon of the solution five or six times a day. This remedy also promotes a good complexion.

Isinglass

Isinglass was a cardinal remedy much used by the Romanies for many complaints. Isinglass is obtained from the swimming bladders of various species of acipenser and is prepared and finely shredded. It used to be sold in various forms under different trade names. The Romanies used it in cases of sleeplessness, brain fatigue and nervous troubles. It was also given to children for rickets and to young persons who used a lot of energy in study. It was used as a 'Brain Food' and travellers in Russia,

Hungary and Romania used the bladder of the sturgeon (which is called Brazilian Islinglass.) A little was rubbed up and put in a glass of hot milk to take last thing at night. An ounce of Isinglass will make about 30 doses.

Insomnia

Infuse a tea from the flowers of the Cowslip (*Primula veris.*) Let it stand for five minutes. This can be added to milk to make a bedtime drink.

Kidney Tonic

Boil one ounce of Cranesbill Root (Geranium malculatum) in one and a half pints of water until the liquid is reduced to one pint, about 20 minutes. Drink a small wineglassful twice a day.

Menstrual Irregularities

Boil two ounces of Blue Cohosh Root (*Calilphyllum thalictroides*) in three pints of water for 20 minutes. Strain and bottle. Drink one wineglassful twice a day

Menstruation - Suppressed

Boil one ounce of Liferoot (*Senecis aureus*) in one pint of water for three minutes. Strain and bottle. Take one tablespoon four or five times a day.

Nasal Congestion and Head Colds

Take one large strong onion and cut in half. Eat one half before going to bed and leave the other half in a saucer beside the bed over night. This will dry up congestion.

Nerves

Mix half an ounce of Potassic Tartrate of Iron in a pint of boiling water and bottle. Take one teaspoon twice a day.

This is also a remedy for lethargy and the 'run-down' feeling. Boil one ounce of Valerian Root (*Valeriana officinalis*) in one and a half pints of water. Reduce to one pint. Take one small wineglassful four or five times a day.

Boil one ounce of Kola Nut (*Cola vera*) in one and a half pints of water for 10 minutes. Strain and bottle. Take a small wineglassful twice daily before meals.

Obesity

Mix together Bladderwrack, Cordova, Boldo and Rhubarb. These can be made into a tea or into tablets. At one time this Romany formula was used to manufacture commercially available tablets.

Piles (Internal)

Boil one ounce of Yellow Dock Root (*Rumex crispus*) in one and a half pints of water. Strain. Drink one wineglassful night and morning.

Piles (External)

Make an ointment of four ounces of pure unsalted lard, one ounce of Plantain leaves and a half dozen leaves of the Ground Ivy. Place together in an enamelled pan and boil over a gentle heat for 10 minutes. Mash the leaves to extract all the goodness. Strain into a jar and cool. Put the ointment freely on the affected area at night.

Pleurisy

Boil one ounce of Pleurisy Root (*Asclepias tuberosa*) in one and a half pints of water for 10 minutes. Strain. Drink a wineglassful two or three times a day.

Rheumatism

Boil one ounce of Dandelion root in one and a half pints of water for 20 minutes. Make up to one pint after allowing to evaporate. Strain. Take a wineglassful twice a day. This is also good for liver disorders.

Sciatica

Infuse a tea of one ounce of Ragwort in one pint of boiling water. Strain and bottle. Take a wineglassful three times a day.

Sickness and Flatulence

Boil one ounce of Spearmint (*Mentha viridis*) in a pint of water for 20 minutes. Take a tablespoonful three or four times a day or whenever sickness is felt.

Sore Throats

Make an infusion of the herb Selfheal (*Prunella vulgaris*) using one ounce to one pint of water. Sip a wineglassful two to three times a day.

Sprains, Muscular Aches and Pains

Mix together one half pint of White Vinegar, one half pint of Turpentine, one quarter pint of Methylated Spirits, two pennyworth of Opodeldso with the whites of two eggs. Bottle and let stand for two days, shaking the bottle at regular intervals.

After two days, the embrocation will be ready.

Mix together one dram of Wintergreen extract with four ounces of Olive Oil and one ounce of Succinic Oil. Shake well before using.

Tonic Stout

Boil one ounce of Nettles, one ounce of Hops and eight ounces of Black (Burnt) Malt in 10 pints of water. Add one quarter of Black Liquorice and two medium-sized potatoes. The potatoes should be washed well but not peeled and should be pricked with a fork. Simmer until reduced to eight pints. Strain into a pan and stir in two ounces of Brown Sugar and one ounce of yeast. The sugar and the yeast should be blended with a little of the liquid before adding to the bulk of the liquor. Stand in a warm place for 24 hours and bottle. Leave a couple of days to create a beautifully creamy stout.

Ulcers (external)

Boil two ounces of White Pond Lily Root (*Nymphoea odorata*) in one pint of water for 20 minutes. Cool. Apply the lotion to ulcers and sores with cotton wool.

For eruptions of the skin. Boil one ounce of Burdock Root (*Arctium lappa*) in one pint of water for five minutes. Take one tablespoon twice a day.

Urinary Complaints

Boil one ounce of Gravel Root (*Eupatorium purpureum*) in one and a half pints of water for 20 minutes. Strain and bottle. Drink a small wineglassful five or six times a day.

Warts, Boils, Cold Sores and Ulcers

Crush a clove of garlic and rub the juice on the affected area. Place the pulp on the affected area and secure with a bandage. Repeat until the wart dries to a scab that can be removed or until the boil has dried up. Put the juice of a garlic clove on cold sores and ulcers. Usually a couple of applications are sufficient.

Wounds and Sores

Make an infusion of the leaves of Comfrey. Bathe the affected area with this. Large colonies of this plant used to cover long stretches of riverbanks and roadside ditches in England and Wales and provided Romany travellers with a constant supply. It is recognised by its drooping bell-like flowers varying in colour from pale yellow to purple. It flowers from May to September.

Chapter Five

Appleby Horse Fair

One coming of summer morning, Alesandro pitched an old army issue bell tent on the edge of the field beyond our back garden. He was a Basque Romany who had travelled the length and breadth of England ever since the last war.

He came to the kitchen door while mother and Ridgey were doing the week's wash. Mother told him that she couldn't afford to pay him for odd jobs but that, in exchange, he would be welcome to take his meals with us and avail himself of what comforts were to be had. This seemed agreeable to him and that was how the front gate was repaired.

Pip was awed by him. I was hopelessly besotted with him. If God made man in His own image it was not that of a white-bearded patriarch. His model was Alesandro.

To me, all grown-ups looked tall so, I have no recollection of Alesandro's height. He had inky, blue-black hair and dark brown eyes. His skin had less of an olive tinge than most of his people but he was darkly tanned most of the time. His was a broad-shouldered, muscular build and I remember him, as one possessed of prodigious strength.

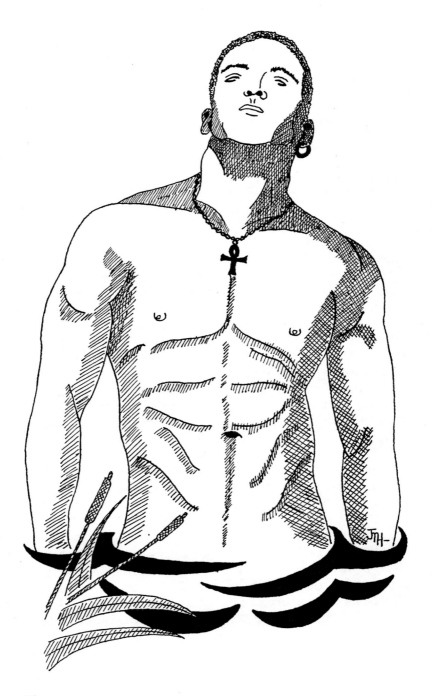

56

Alesandro bent down and pulled the ankh forward from my chest. "I know this sign," he said, "it is good".

Alesandro was travelling north for the Appleby Horse Fair. The Fair has taken place in early June since 1751. Before that, an April Charter Fair was established in 1685. It is the largest traditional horse-fair still in existence and it is also the largest annual Romany gathering in the country although, these days, there are fewer genuine Romanies at the event than in those days long ago. The central event is the big sale on the second Wednesday of the month. Romanies begin to arrive from all over the country for weeks beforehand and the roads and lanes thereabouts become choked with their horses and ponies, vardoes and trailers. Harness races are held before the big sale. A great many more people go to the fair than those who buy or sell horses and fairground hucksters take advantage of the gathering.

Having agreed all with my mother who knew, without fear, that he would see me safe there and back, I walked out one May morning with Alesandro. Back-packed and kitted out, we were on our way to the Appleby Horse Fair. Mine was a sense of the wonder of the world and Alesandro fed it from his store of stories and his vast knowledge of nature.

At night, Alesandro pitched our tent and cooked the fish we'd caught or the rabbits we'd bolted on an open fire and told me all about the Romany life as the stars looked down. And when my feet were sore, he rubbed them with Gypsy Foot Ointment.

We bathed in the Hodder below Hindburndale. "Always bathe in moving water," Alesandro advised, "never in water that is still".

We joined the vardo of Alesandro's friends above Bowland Knotts and there was no more walking to Appleby. As we bumped along, Alesandro made me acquainted with the Stone bramble, Red campion, Cross-leaved heath, Whinchat and Willow Warbler.

So we arrived, along with many others, at Appleby-in-Westmorland. It is a small but lovely town. It is commandeered for the Horse Fair for an entire week and the locals have grown to resent it. At this time, many of them get away on holiday to avoid it.

In that June week, Gipsies gallop their horses through the River Eden to wash them, conduct some frenzied horse-dealing, drink copiously (one Romany of my acquaintance could drink a bottle of whisky at one go with little effect) and, on occasion, get into fights. But despite the ambience of violence about the event, it is invariably a family affair. A self-appointed council of Gipsies liaises with police and local authority to monitor trouble and pay for any damage.

For many Romanies, the Fair is a chance to see and be seen, a time to renew friendships (Alesandro's motivation), settle disputes and display possessions. The wealthy bank their money in possessions and thus avoid the scrutiny of the tax man. For many, money comes from dealing in scrap metal done with hard cash by dealers constantly on the move. Nowadays those possessions include some very expensive cars. Ornate caravans and antique vardoes are camped on the hill overlooking the town.

About 7,000 Gipsies and travelling folk stake out a few square feet of campsite in a few hedged acres. Caravans and vardoes are arranged along a main thoroughfare. At the top and bottom, traders set out their stalls and sell tack, souveniers and clothing. The fortune-tellers take up the middle stretch.

Romanies move about in a carnival atmosphere examining and discussing horses. The hill swirls with people, horses and traps in clouds of dust or a sea of mud.

A daily ritual that draws large crowds is the washing of the horses in the river. The river and its banks froth with soapsuds. Bronzed men strip to the waist and wade in with pants and riding boots on. They leap onto the horses' backs and urge them into deep water. Then, an aquatic rodeo begins.

In the Town Square, horses, carts and Gipsies mill around in a confused mass. Hugely muscled men sit with their womenfolk and argue, sing, bargain and hand around plump baby sons for admiration. The pubs do a roaring trade but many are stripped of everything moveable before their doors are opened. Closing time is ignored and the bars are so tightly packed that the drunks have no room to fall down.

Horses are trotted up and down before potential buyers. All of a sudden, sticks and whips are cracked on hindquarters to whip the horses into a frenzy. When calm is restored, the bargaining begins. It's cash on the nail for purchases and a good deal of hand-slapping goes on.

Romany horses are among the most disciplined in the world. A display of bad temper from a horse is taken as a personal insult and some Romanies still resort to the use of a twitch as a means of control.

In the evening, trotting races are held by the river, bets are placed and the event draws a large crowd.

On the last night of the Fair, Romanies come down the hill to gather in the square by the church. The end is celebrated with singing, dancing and drinking.

Anyone who lives with and for horses could only be carried away by all the excitement and colour.

Alesandro engaged in the good-humoured banter about the merits of this or that horse and, together, we looked at all the stalls and engaged in the general feeling of camaraderie.

During the day, I was ever at his side. At night, and nights were warm that June, Alesandro tucked me up on a ground sheet beneath his friend's vardo. The rest of the evening was his own and he would go off to a pub in the town.

On just one such sleepless night, I dogged his tacks, followed like an expert tracker at a safely unobservable distance.

I watched him through the halfly tinted panes of the pub's windows, pinned him with my eyes through the smokey fog.

Alesandro was engaged in conversation with several other Romany men when a rather drunk diddikai became pushy with him. The diddikai punctuated each point with a finger to Alesandro's broad chest.

I watched as Alesandro's friends withdrew and Alesandro went into a cool simmer. Then, all of a sudden and to everyone's amazement, Alesandro lifted the diddikai kicking and squirming into the air and marched him over the heads of everyone to the pub door. Alesandro did not relinquish his hold until he got to the Eden, then he pitched the diddikai into the water to the collective applause of all who followed.

Returning, his eye fell on me agog with admiration and scooped me up in his cabled arms.

"That's enough excitement for one night, little man," he laughed, "back to bed with you."

"Your son?" asked one of his mates.

"Yes," Alesandro hissed through gritted teeth, "he's mine."

As he carried me away, Alesandro looked into my face with extraordinary tenderness and whispered, "I've touched your soul, you'll always be mine."

Alesandro and I travelled back with his friends as far as Long Preston. We stopped to wash the dust away in Toside Beck before making our last camp of the journey.

As Alesandro stooped to splash his naked body, I noticed for the first time a series of numbers on his left wrist. At first, I thought it was a tattoo but then I realised that it was a brand. I was mesmerised by it.

Rising up, the water cascading from his lanky hair, Alesandro caught my stare. He instantly slapped his right hand over his left wrist and that broke the spell. There he stood in the beauty of his nakedness and all that he felt shame for was that brand on his wrist. Then, as he turned away, he laughed. It wasn't the laughter of joy. It was a dark laughter spun from the notes of despair.

We were taught not to ask personal questions and, so, I had to wait until mother told me what Alesandro's brand meant and until I was old enough to understand. Alesandro had been in a Nazi concentration camp in the final days of the war. Not just the Jews but Romanies, homosexuals and any others Hitler deemed to be undesirable or impure died in Nazi gas chambers and concentration camps. Alesandro's wife and son died as Buckenwald was being liberated.

So Alesandro saw me home safe. He stayed on for a further week before heading south. We remained on his itinerary for the next couple of years and, then, one summer we didn't see him nor did we ever hear what became of him after that.

From time to time, I would sit on the drystone wall and look out to where Alesandro used to pitch his tent. I missed him and that brand still bothers me.

Chapter Six

Romany Vet, Romany Poacher

The Romany Horse

The horse always used to be central to Romany life. Romany men are usually excellent judges of horseflesh and Romany children often learn to ride from a very early age. But it used to be said, "never buy a horse from a Gipsy." Their skill in turning out a broken down old nag as a lively thoroughbred is legend. In Romany medicine there are a number of equine remedies.

Broken-Wind (asthma in horses)

A condition regarded as incurable by vets but Romanies used a mixture of Aniseed, Wood tar and treacle to greatly lessen the inconvenience. An infusion of twist tobacco or shag (one ounce to one and a half pints of boiling water) was said to do the same.

Bog Spavin

Found most commonly in cart horses. It occurs in young horses that have been overfed or forced. If lameness is present, a hot poultice of common nettle is applied. If not, a dressing of green tar.

Colic

Oil of Turpentine and ground ginger made into balls with flour. Or, a purge of Aloes and soap followed by a dose of Fennel oil in weak spirits. Or, two ounces of Turpentine to one pint of Linseed oil followed (after 15 minutes) by a quart of warm beer.

Coughs

Black treacle in warm water.

Cracked Heels

A poultice of Linseed until the discharge ceases followed by washing with a solution of Alum and crystallised Ferrous Sulphate. Finally, apply Wood tar and a healing ointment. If attended by a fever, make a strong infusion of Agrimony leaves.

Mange

A solution of sulphur and lime in water applied at five day intervals.

Quittor (a disease of the foot)

Bread poultices applied cold followed by a poultice of bruised Plantain leaves and liberal applications of cold water. When inflammation is gone, apply an ointment of Marshmallow.

Sprains and Sores

A liniment of Methylated Spirits, oil of Turpentine and Camphor. For slight abrasions, an ointment of Marshmallow.

Staggers (a stomach disorder)
A purge of Aloes and warm water. Or, a purge of liquorice powder, soap and black treacle. Plenty of warm water to drink but no food for a day.

Thrush (foot thrush)
Butter of Antimony (Antimony trichloride) to remove decaying matter. Bathe with salt water and dress with an ointment of Marshmallow mixed with charcoal.

Thormbi (causes leg swellings)
Regular doses of Turpentine and the juice of juniper berries. Complete rest.

Worms
Bay, laurel or broom tops, dried and powdered and administered each day in scalded bran. Normally takes about a fortnight to cure.

The Romany Dog
Some Romanies regard dogs (and cats too) as mochardi (unclean) because they lick themselves. Yet they are happy to eat the meat a dog thieves for them. Perhaps roasting it is a form of purification. However, I have known many Romany men who do not regard their dogs as mochardi.

The relationship between the Romany and his dog was a unique one. There was much more of a sense of comrade-ship based on survival and subsistence than the pet-master relationship.

The Bedlington Terrier's endurance and racing-hound speed made it a long-standing companion to poachers. It was nicknamed the Gipsy Dog. It could go after otter, run down a rabbit and hold its own in a dog fight.

More commonly, Romany dogs were mongrels and, generally, less troublesome healthwise than many pure breeds.

The Romany dog was a one-man dog. He hunted and poached with his master and guarded the vardo at night.

Not surprisingly, the Romanies had a stock of remedies for their dogs as well as themselves.

Distemper
Give the dog ordinary brewer's yeast. A small dose every morning.

To Prevent Distemper
Give the dog a small piece of raw potato from time to time.

For Mange
Make an ointment using two drams of powdered Boracic Acid, 60 grams of Thymol and two ounces of soft Paraffin. Rub this well into the skin every day.

Worm Prevention and Conditioner
Roll a small piece of hard tobacco in a piece of dough. Administer this on a regular basis. Young dogs have a natural liking for tobacco and will eat the tobacco from cigarettes. They do not, however, like the smell of tobacco smoke.

For Poisoning

First give the dog about 15 grains of emetic tartar. This will induce vomiting. When vomiting has finished, give the dog two ounces of Caster Oil.

For Sore Pads

Dogs that run a lot get a complaint that makes their nails crack underneath. Make a brine of one ounce of common rock salt to one quart of warm water. Wash the dog's feet in the solution. Then, paint the pads and nail quicks with Arnica.

For Fleas and Ticks

Boil two ounces of Quassis Chips in two and a half pints of water for a couple of minutes. Add two ounces of crushed Stavesacre Seeds and two ounces of Acetic Acid to the solution while it is cooling. Strain. Sponge the dog with this solution every day for a week. Use once every fourteen days as a preventative.

Worming

Do not feed the dog after midday. The next morning give him grated Areca nut with a piece of butter. When he wants a drink give him the water that carrots have been boiled in. Do not feed the dog for four hours after he has had the Areca nut. This can also be used as a preventative.

Coat Conditioner

Shake Boracic Acid Powder from a pepper pot into the coat. Rub in well with the fingertips. Leave the powder in for about an hour, then brush out. This will also prevent the dog from scratching.

To Earn a Dog's Loyalty

Put a piece of soft bread under the armpit. When it is permeated with your scent and perspiration, give it to the dog.

The Romany Poacher

Once upon a time, aspects of Romany subsistence were synonymous with poaching. In this, it has to be understood that the Romanies, who were nomadic, regarded the whole world as their larder. They were seldom conscious law-breakers. The roguish element, however, did resort to downright criminal activities in the procurement of food. New Forest Gipsies used to cram wool into sheep's mouths causing them to suffocate. The farmer would take this as a natural phenomenon and put it down to the stupidity of the sheep. Some Hungarian Gipsies poisoned pigs and were not in the least phased by the eating of carrion - mulo mas. But most Romanies simply had a disregard for the artificial boundaries established by sedentary folk. They were not wasteful of natural resources and only took what they needed when they needed it.

Bait For Catching Eels and Trout

Use equal parts of Oil of Rodium, Oil of Juniper and Oil of Cedarwood. Sprinkle a little over a handful of moss and place the worms in the moss for at least 12 hours. If using another bait, mix a drop of the combined oils with it.

Bait For Roach and Perch

Use equal parts of Oil of Spike, Oil of Fennel and Oil of Thyme. Mix well. Use just a drop to any living or other bait.

For Bolting Rabbits From Their Holes

Take some course brown paper and cut it into strips about two inches wide and 18 inches long. Make a solution from four ounces of Saltpetre, half an ounce of Cayenne Pepper and enough vinegar to mix to a paste. Brush the paste over the paper and roll the paper into loose rolls. Dry the rolls before using them. Place a roll of paper into a rabbit hole on the windward side and light it. When it is fully alight, lay a piece of turf over the hole. Place a net over the bolt-holes. If netting rather than shooting, make sure that nets are placed over bolt-holes before lighting the paper.

For Drawing Rabbits and Hares to Your Fields

Mix together one quarter ounce of Oil of Parsley, one dram of Oil of Angelica, one dram of Oil of Aniseed and one half ounce of Oil of Copaida. Put a few drops on pieces of wood and twigs and put these down where you want the animals to come.

To Repel Rats and Mice

Soak pieces of calico in Spirits of Tar and place these in the entrance to each run.

Chapter Seven

More Romany Lore

It is a fact that there is more folklore about Romanies than there is Romany folklore. Fact and fiction become inextricably jumbled together when the subject of Gipsies comes up. Some of this lore centres on supposed magical powers. For instance, Gipsies have the gift of second sight, they can cure disease, protect houses from fire, tell fortunes and see into the future, understand the language of horses and have been known to give up their lives for their horses. It is said that Romany coppersmiths bare their heads to the new moon. Gipsies save clay-lined thrushes nests to collect milk stolen from cattle, they kidnap children, are petty thieves and that their women are promiscuous. In fact, Romany women are generally very chaste.

Many Romany customs reflect the practices and beliefs of the countries they have lived in. Romany marriage customs, burial rites, childbirth and menstrual taboos are similar to those customs found elsewhere among other peoples. They also believe in ghosts, omens and the evil eye as do many other peoples. They used to avoid having their photographs taken because they believed the soul was separable. They had private names and public names so that they could not be bewitched by an incantation using their name.

It has been said that the Romanies brought nothing, originated nothing, but adopted what they found in every country they visited as it appealed to them. This is really a gross exaggeration; in fact, the Romanies are people who have maintained their own way of life and code of behaviour and spiritual values in the face of centuries of persecution.

An old proverb says "when you cut a Gipsy in ten pieces you have not killed him; you have merely made ten Gipsies." The proverb is significant when the Gipsy cult of the dead is understood. Romanies believe that the soul of the dead is not freed from this world until the body is burned. Otherwise, the dead can return to reproach the living sometimes in the form of a vampire. Despite prohibitions in Hungary, Romanies disinterred their dead and secretly burned them. In Germany, Gipsies searched out the graves of their kin and burned their bodies to liberate their souls. Not even the death penalty could prevent Romanies from performing this last sacred rite. With but slight variations, Romany burial customs are the same everywhere.

The tale is told that Romanies were forced to wander the earth because they refused the Holy Family a refuge when they fled Bethlehem. Another tale comes from a medieval work that says that when Joseph and Mary took the infant Jesus and fled into Egypt, they were met by an old Gipsy woman who offered them shelter in her stable. In another story, after Pharaoh conquered the world he challenged God. God opened the side of a mountain and created a great gale that blew Pharaoh and his armies into it. The mountain closed upon them. After that, alien armies drove the remaining Egyptians into Spain.

In Romania, the tale is told that the Gipsies were cursed because one of their smiths made the nails for Christ's cross. But the Gipsies countered with their own story. The Gipsy smith made the nails so thin that they would give little pain. Mary blessed them with the words that their work should be light and their profit great. In another tale, a Gypsy woman tried to steal the nails to prevent the crucifixion. She could only get away with one of them and that is why only three nails were used.

Many Romany customs are linked to Pagan Carrying Out or Killing Death mimes. One custom of Southern Europe, which used to be observed on the fourth Sunday of Lent, was called Sawing the Old Woman. It was adopted by Gipsies in the area as a Palm Sunday observance. A puppet dressed as the Old Woman was beaten, sawn in two and finally burned. The ashes were saved and thrown into the next cemetery the tribe came to. A vague association can be traced to the Shadow Queen who vanishes in the spring to return in the winter.

Many Gipsies were masons in Italy. They buried the shadow of a man in the foundations of a new house. British Romanies do not eat hares. In their belief the hare is a vampire. Gipsy women leap into their husband's graves and lie there for a few minutes (a throw back to ancient Hindu sati.) They are not allowed to remarry.

In general, Romany folklore is the folklore of Europe with a Gipsy twist and flavour.

Perhaps the one Romany accessory uppermost in the minds of most people is the vardo; the Gipsy's travelling home. These are becoming a thing of the past, to be replaced by all mod-cons mobile homes. The decorating of the traditional vardo was a centuries old art that rivalled canal boat art in its flamboyance. One of the earliest descriptions of such a conveyance in English literature is from Charles Dickens' *The Old Curiosity Shop*.

"It was not a shabby, dingy, dusty cart, but a smart little house upon wheels, with white dimity curtains festooning the windows and window shutters of green picked out with panels of a staring red, in which happily-contrasted colours the whole concern shone brilliant. Neither was it a poor caravan drawn by a single donkey or emaciated horse, for a pair of horses in pretty good condition were released from the shafts and grazing on the frowzy grass. One half of it. was carpeted and so partitioned off at the further end as to accommodate a sleeping place, constructed after the fashion of a berth on board ship, which was shaded, like the little window, with fair white curtains and looked comfortable enough. The other half served for a kitchen and was fitted up with a stove whose small chimney passed through the roof and a few cooking utensils and articles of crockery. These latter necessaries hung upon the walls."

In English literature of the 19th Century, Gipsies were often cast as villains. The novelist William Harrison Ainsworth coloured his books, most notably *Rookwood* (1834) and *Mervyn Clitheroe* (1857), with Romany Rogues. In this century, D.H.Lawrence used a Gipsy (in *The Virgin And The Gipsy*) as a signature for uninhibited male sexuality.

Ainsworth's novels are steeped in the supernatural. In Roodwood, besides "a motley assemblage of tawny-skinned varlets, dark-eyed women and children whose dusky limbs betrayed their lineage, in strange costume", there is also Barbara Lovel, a sorceress, "wrapped in a cloak composed of the skins of various animals". She has the gift of prophecy.

For many people, the words "Gipsy" and "Fortune Telling" are synonymous. The Christian church is ambivalent, to say the least, and downright condemnatory of such practices as fortune-telling. Formal religion has had no great influence on the Romanies and Pagan traditions are as strong, if not stronger, than Christian dogma with many of them.

Romany women tell fortunes while they hawk their other wares from door to door. Gipsy fortune-tellers are still a recognizable presence at fairs, seaside resorts and county shows. None of these have any difficulty obtaining clients even when the prevalent public mood is one of incredulity. Gipsies have been fortune-tellers as far back as we have any records of them and they have done more to spread belief in sympathetic magic and prognostication than any other race on earth. The Romanies have acquired considerable skill in reading character and anticipating thought. That being said, I have known some Gipsies I believed were quite genuine in their gift of prophesy.

Charles Leland listed fourteen "hokibens" (deceits) whch are invariably true of almost anyone who has reached middle age:

1. Many middle-aged men have been involved in a law suit or property dispute.

2. Something of great advantage will come their way, but they must watch for the opportunity.

3. They will have three great chances in their lives.

4. Someone of wealth and beauty is in love with them.

5. They have had great trouble at one time with relatives.

6. They have been in danger of death three times.

7. They have had an enemy who has caused them much trouble.

8. By doing a good deed they have got into trouble.

9. Their passions have caused them trouble three times.

10. They will meet someone who will have a great influence on their lives if they cultivate the friendship.

11. They will find something valuable if they are vigilant.

12. They have done much good for which others have been ungrateful.

13. They have had several love affairs.

14. They have a great capacity for something, which will reveal itself.

In fortune-telling, the palm or the Tarot are used, but the palm is more commonly used by British Gipsies. Fortune-telling was and is used as a cover for confidence tricks - the hokano baro. However, when all the deceptions are discounted in Romany fortune-telling there is still a great deal that remains honest and true.

When Carrotty Dick, so called for his orange-red hair, a local farm hand consulted mother, she could not erase the constant image of a body of water. Two days later, Dick fell down the well.

Chapter Eight

A Romany Larder

Whenever Romanies travelled in the British countryside they were near a source of wild foods. Nature offers an abundance of foodstuffs in hedgerows, woodlands, meadows, heaths, moorlands and coasts.

Laver and carageen, both seaweeds, and samphire, from shingly Norfolk beaches, provide a coastal resource.

Fields, riverbanks and streams provide Fat Hen, Sorrel, Nettle, Watercress and Mint. Woods, hedges and roadsides provide Hazel Nuts, Blackberry, Dandelion, Elder and Sweet Chestnut. Heaths and moors provide Rowan, Bilberry and Thyme.

Generally, Romanies regard all fungi with suspicion. They do eat the giant puff-ball (*Hycoperdon borista)* although this is considered poor fare. The tender young puff-ball is sliced, fried in dripping and garnished with onions and herbs. Rowena Farre, who wrote *Seal Morning,* pronounced this delicious. In its dry state, the puff-ball was used by Romanies to staunch wounds. For the same purpose, they also used Touchwood (*Polyporous igniarius)* - both make very good styptics. Once, Gipsies made good use of poisonous fungi.

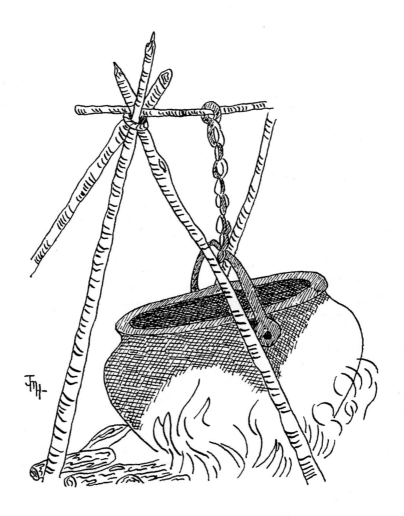

Even when equipped with stoves in vardoes and caravans, Romanies prefer to cook on an open fire out of doors. Food tends to be stewed and fried and the dishes of the countries they have travelled in are often adapted for this purpose.

Kettle Broth
(Serves six)

1 $^1/_2$ ounces of bacon fat

2 onions, peeled and chopped

8 ounces of leeks, thinly sliced

2 $^1/_2$ ounces of sliced white bread (crusts removed)

2 pints of chicken stock

Salt

Ground Black Pepper

$^1/_2$ Pint of milk

Melt the bacon fat in a large, heavy-based pan. Cook the onions and leeks until soft and transparent. Add the bread and stock and boil. Season with salt and pepper, cover and simmer for 30 minutes. Pass through a sieve to purée and add enough milk to give the broth the consistency of thin cream. Cooking time 50 minutes in all.

Trout With Bacon
(Serves six)

6 medium sized Trout

Salt and pepper

12 thin rashers of smoked bacon

1 tablespoon of chopped parsley

Clean Trout and season inside. Remove the rind from the bacon and place the rashers in a large, heavy skillet. Lay the Trout head to tail on top of the layer of bacon. Season with salt, pepper and parsley. Cover and cook for 20 minutes.

Grilled Eel
(Serves two)

1 pound of Eel
Salt
Bay leaves
3 tablespoons of melted bacon fat

Salt and cut the Eel into one-inch pieces. Put the pieces on skewers placing bay leaves between each piece. Brush the Eel with bacon fat and lay on a hot griddle pan. Cook for about five minutes each side or until the flesh begins to part from the bone. Can be served with lemon and brown bread and butter.

Boiled Bacon Dinner
(Serves four)

One small joint of Bacon
2 pounds of small potatoes, scrubbed but not peeled
1 pound of green cabbage or spring greens
Whole Black Peppercorns
Juniper berries
Bay leaves
Whole Grain Mustard

Soak the joint in water with Bay leaves, Juniper berries and whole black peppercorns for three to four hours. Remove and place in a deep pan with the whole potatoes.

Cover with water and bring to the boil. Simmer until bacon joint is tender and potatoes are cooked. Add the cabbage or greens, finely chopped, and cook until tender. Drain water and serve the meal with whole grain mustard.

Fried Young Rabbit
(Serves four)

2 young Rabbits, jointed
2 ounces of bacon fat
8 ounces of young green nettle tops, washed and chopped
Salt
Ground Black Pepper
Thyme

Heat the bacon fat in a lidded frying pan and cook the rabbit joints until nearly done. Season with salt, pepper and thyme and add the chopped nettles. Cover and cook until nettles are tender and reduced in the juices. Overall cooking time about 30 minutes.

Steamed Nettles
(Serves four)

2 pounds of young nettles
2 ounces of unsalted butter
Sea Salt
Ground Black Pepper

Wash the nettles and discard the stalks. Place in a colander over a pan of boiling water. Stream until tender. Coat with butter and season with salt and pepper. Cooking time about 20 minutes.

Nettles can also be fried in butter.

Pan Haggerty

(Serves four)

1 pound of peeled potatoes
2 ounces of dripping
8 ounces of finely chopped onions
Sea Salt
Ground Black Pepper
4 ounces of grated cheddar cheese

Grate the potatoes and press out the surplus starch on a cloth. Melt the dripping in a deep, heavy frying pan and add the onions. Fry these until soft and transparent. Remove the onions. Cover the pan with grated potatoes and spread the onions over these. Season with salt and pepper and sprinkle with grated cheese. Cook until the bottom browns. Turn gently to brown the other side. Serve hot from the pan. Cooking time about 20 minutes.

Colcannon

(Serves four to six)

1 pound of shredded green cabbage
1 ^{1}/₂ pounds of hot, mashed potatoes
2 spring onions, finely chopped
2 fluid ounces of milk
Salt
Ground Black Pepper
2 ounces of butter (unsalted)

Cook the cabbage until tender. Mix in the potato, onion and milk to make a firm, smooth mixture. Season. Fry in the butter until the edges are crisp and the mixture browns. Cooking time about 20 minutes.

Hedgerow Jelly
(Yields four to five pounds)

3 pounds of Windfall Apples (or cooking apples)
2 pounds of Blackberries
2 pounds of Damsons
Juice of one whole Lemon
Sugar

Roughly chop the peeled apples into a large, heavy-based pan and add the blackberries and damsons. Add enough cold water to cover the fruit. Add the lemon juice. Bring to a boil and then simmer until the fruit breaks down. Strain through a scalded jelly bag without pressing for at least four hours. Warm the sugar. Add one pound of sugar for each pint of strained juice. Bring to a boil and cook rapidly until setting point is reached. Skim, pot and seal.

Romanies love pork in its many forms but for travelling it is usually salted or smoked. The Hungarian Mulo Mas is pork that has been allowed to become rancid before cooking.

More often than not everything available goes into the fireside pot to make a stew for cold evenings.

Breakfast in England is much the same as for Gorgios - bacon and eggs. As Ainsworth wrote in *Rookwood*, "a thin column of pale blue smoke, that arose in curling wreaths from out the brake..... That smoke holds out a prospect of breakfast."

Chapter Nine

Some Romany Tales

Goulies and ghosties and the boggart at the top of Pendle Water, witches and warlocks, pirates and swashbucklers, highwaymen and Gipsies - for Pip and I, these were the stuff of our childhood. Reading aloud around the winter hearth, seances on wet afternoons, ghostly tales at bedtime and Romany of the BBC wove a magic tapestry for us.

Romany was one Bramwell Evens, a Methodist minister of Romany extraction who broadcast a slot in the Children's Hour. The first broadcast went out from Manchester in 1933. His programme went nationwide in 1938 and spawned a series of popular books of which I still have some. For a long time, it was a well kept secret that Romany's travels were studio made but this did nothing to diminish the programme's popularity. Nor did it matter much to us that Romany's vardo was not a vardy at all but an Irish navvie's cart. We were uncritical of the spell he cast.

Romanies are great storytellers. They have a strong sense of the bizarre, absurd and ridiculous but most of their tales have a moral - are instructive. Such tales are a school for those peoples whose way of life is based on an oral tradition.

Frosty

An old man named Frosty was walking along a road with his hat cocked to one side when he met another man. This man was lying on his stomach with his ear to the ground.

"Are you something of a fool to be doing what you are doing," Frosty asked.

"I am not a fool," the man responded, "I am listening to the Members of Parliament in London making speeches."

"You could be of use to me," replied Frosty, "your hearing is excellent."

The two of them walked on together until they met another man shouldering his gun.

"What are you doing," Frosty asked.

"Can't you see it," Shoot-well replied, "I am going to shoot that fly on that rock over there in America."

"You could be of use too," said Frosty, "come with us."

The three men walked on until they came upon a man with swelled chest, blowing through puckered lips.

"What are you doing," Frosty asked.

"There is no wind to turn the sails of that mill yonder," the fourth man replied, "I am providing it."

"You could be of use to me," said Frosty, "come with us."

As they walked along they came to a fifth man who was carrying one of his legs under his arm.

"What are you doing," Frosty asked.

"I pulled off my leg so that I couldn't run too fast," the fifth man replied.

"You must come with us," Frosty replied.

As they went on they encountered a sixth man. He was a big, strong man and he was carrying a huge tree on his shoulder. Frosty asked him to come with them.

When they came to a town, they heard that the king had an old witch at his court who was a swift runner. A reward was offered to any man who could outrun her.

"Let's go to the palace," Frosty suggested.

So they went to the palace and Frosty put up his running man, Run-well, against the king's witch.

The next day the race was run. The old witch was beating Run-well so Shoot-well shot a dart into her knee and Run-well won the race.

The king was furious. "Who are these men," he indignantly asked.

The old witch told the king to proclaim that he desired the lake in front of the palace to be drained dry on the morrow.

The six men were accommodated in the palace again that night and as they were preparing for bed Hear-well overheard this and told Frosty.

The next morning the king told Frosty and his men that he wanted the lake drained. Frosty summoned Blow-well and

Blow-well blew the lake dry. He even blew all the mud and stones out of it and left it bare.

The king did not know what to do about these powerful men and he feared them. He decided to lodge them in an old iron chamber and kindle a fire beneath it to turn it into an oven to roast them to death. As night fell, the king ushered the six into the chamber and suggested that they might be more comfortable sleeping there.

"This seems a warm room," Frosty responded, "we will sleep here."

"Yes it is a warm room," the king laughed, " and it will be warmer still soon!"

The king closed the iron door and the six men sat down to chat before going to sleep. The room became hotter and hotter so Frosty cocked his hat and the men began to shiver with cold. The room cooled and they all lay down to sleep.

When the king returned in the morning he was amazed to find them alive. He called the six out to have their breakfast. When they finished their meal the king said, "I want a ship built upon the lake. I want this done before tomorrow morning."

When the morning came, the ship had been built. The king said, "I want the ship to sail without water." Frosty summoned Blow-well and Blow-well blew the ship out of sight.

"How much money do you want to leave my kingdom," the king asked.

"As much as one of my servants can carry away," Frosty replied.

Strong-man arrived with a sack and the king had it half filled. "That's as much as you can carry," the king said.

Strong-man lifted the sack with one hand; "this trifle is not heavy. Fill it!"

The king scowled but had the sack filled. "Be off and come here no more."

When they were gone, the king fell into a rage at the loss of his treasure. He sent his soldiers in pursuit.

Hear-well heard them coming and warned the others. Frosty told them not to fear. He cocked his hat and the soldiers were frozen to the spot. Frosty paid off his men and went home to his village where he bought himself a little house and did very well.

Orange and Lemon

(Romany tales frequently incorporate little ditties that the teller pauses to sing making the whole an entertainment)

There once were two daughters, Orange and Lemon. Their mother liked Lemon best and the father preferred Orange. The mother made Orange do all the dirty work as soon as the father turned his back.

One day, the mother sent Orange to fetch the milk. "If you break the pitcher, I will kill you," she threatened.

As Orange was returning she tripped and fell and broke the pitcher. When she came home she hid in the passage.

When her mother came out, she saw the broken pitcher and the spilt milk. She grabbed Orange and dragged her into the house. Orange cried, "oh mother, oh mother, don't kill me!"

But her mother threw her on the block and chopped off her head. She cooked it for dinner and served it to her husband for a sheep's head.

"Where is Orange," the father asked.

"She has not come home from school yet," the mother replied.

But the father did not believe her. He went upstairs and found Orange's fingers in a box. He was so overcome that he fainted.

Orange's spirit flew away to the jeweller's shop and sang-

> My mother chopped my head off,
> My father picked my bones,
> My little sister buried me,
> Beneath cold marble stones.

"Sing that again," said the jeweller, "and I'll give you a gold watch." So Orange sang again and flew off with the watch to the bootshop. She sang her song to the bootmaker and he gave her a pair of boots. She sang her song to the stonemason and he gave her a piece of marble as big as her head.

Orange flew off home with her things, sat on the chimney and called down it.

Father, Father, come to me,
And I will show thee what I've got for thee!

He came and she sent down the gold watch. Then Orange called down the chimney again.

Sister, Sister, come to me,
And I will show thee what I've got for thee!

Lemon came and Orange sent down the pair of boots. Then Orange called down the chimney again.

Mother, Mother, come to me,
And I will show thee what I've got for thee!

The mother put her head up the chimney and down came the block of marble and killed her.

Orange came down the chimney and lived happily ever after with her father and Lemon.

Shadow Man

(The Shadow Man occurs in a number of forms in Romany lore. There are several versions of this tale but I prefer this one because it reminds me of someone I once knew.)

Jerry the Greek was a man with no imagination. It was beyond any stretching of his mind and conscious to conceive what effect any action of his might have on others. Quite the contrary, everything that ever happened

to him was someone else's fault. He never accepted blame and he never said sorry. Jerry the Greek was all things to everyone but nothing to anyone in particular. But that's the way he wanted it. Beyond a minimal cordiality, he wanted nothing to do with others - that way, at least, he was sure of emotional invulnerability. By subtle means of hurt, Jerry kept others at a distance - so distant that even his wife walked out on him. In effect, no one knew the real Jerry - not even Jerry.

Jerry's vardo was monastic - purely functional. His one concession to frippery was his music and he filled his solitude with music because it called for no introspection and no serious thought beyond keeping time - he fiddled well!

Oh yes, Jerry fiddled well. Every evening after his supper he would sit before his vardo and play many a tune. But in his mind he never heard the words. He didn't want any words, words required feeling and he didn't want to feel.

It was just such a night with the moon at its most full casting long shadows in the copse that something struck Jerry as very strange. It jarred on the conscious so much that he stopped fiddling. He had the moon full behind him in a clear sky but he could not see his own shadow before him. The realisation dropped on his mind like a sounding bell and he leapt to his feet. Turning swiftly, Jerry saw his shadow behind him and was chilled to the marrow. Shadow appeared to be standing with a noose in his hand. But then, all of a sudden, Shadow evaporated and when Jerry turned back he caught its cast just as it should be.

Jerry the Greek was so unnerved by his experience that he called it a night and retired to the womb-like security of his vardo bed.

Long before the dawning light, Jerry awoke in a cold sweat. To his horror he saw his own shadow dancing on the vardo walls singing -

Clanger, clanger, doppleganger,
Would not lose both friend and wife,
Clanger, clanger, doppelganger,
Would not be afraid of life,
Would not fear the pain of loving,
Would not fear the joy of giving,
Would not fear each day of living.

And as the shadow danced it swung the noose about in the air. Jerry cried out and pulled the covers over his head. The first rays of the morning sun streamed through the vardo window and Jerry sighed with relief. All seemed as normal and Jerry the Greek, a man of no imagination, put the incident down to an overworked one.

Throughout the day, Jerry drew reassurance from the proper cast of his shadow.

That night was overcast and there was no moon. The only shadows that danced on Jerry's camp came from the naked flames of his fire. And yet, Jerry could not shake the uneasy feeling that he was being watched. Jerry fiddled a few tunes and then decided to turn in.

As the night went on, the sky cleared and the moon shone bright through the vardo window.

Jerry awoke in cold terror, spluttering and choking. Shadow pinched the noose even tighter around Jerry's blueing neck.

"Why fear death," said Shadow, "you died long ago. This is just the last rite."

Shadow hauled the struggling Jerry from his bed and secured the noose to one of the roof struts. Jerry the Greek kicked out as he dangled a mere foot from the vardo floor and then he was still.

When the morning came, Shadow leaped from the vardo door and pranced around the clearing, singing, "free, free to live the life my shadow denied." And as he danced and sang, Shadow became a man of substance.

Chapter Ten

Oubliette

We used to play at being Gipsies, my mate and I. Robbie was Romany entire but I had to coca my face from the Cadbury's tin on the kitchen shelf and black my hair from the tin of boot-black. Washing this out caused my mother considerable annoyance.

Tight knee-breeches, shirts knotted across our bellies, and red and white polka-dot kerchiefs made us look just like the picture in the village reading-room's copy of *The Romany Rye*. Then we moved on to play at being sailors so I started reading *Two Years Before The Mast* and Robin started reading *Mister Midshipman Easy*. I say "we" but really I followed Robin in everything - he was my closest friend. If he decided to sail the high seas then I was bound and determined to sign on as his first mate.

"Cabin-boy!" Robin ordered.

"Oh, no you don't. I've been on the short end of the stick an awful lot lately!"

"All right matey - I'll be captain and you can be my lieutenant." The atmosphere relaxed again. Robin was always more calmly down to earth, even when we were dreaming, than I was. He could always take command of a situation and brought to it his strength and masculine good-humour. But then, he was two years older than I.

We both had one place in common. A place we dearly loved. Not a secret place because it was always frequented by travellers and trekkers. The Nick of Pendle slumbers a lion-shape furred in clumps of rushes and sedge to stretch out on a bleak, sweeping moorland. The best view from it is over the Plain of Fylde to the Irish Sea. A rough gritstone track provides an exhilarating walk. Residents of this high place number rabbits, hares, Swaledale sheep, meadow pipits, skylarks and lapwings. The ubiquitous cloudberry provided a delicious orange-coloured fruit for us to pick and eat on our climb. This was our castle, our sailing ship, our battlefield and our Gipsy encampment.

"There aren't anymore unicorns, Robbie!"

"Are you getting deep again? Don't be silly, Plato!"

I could feel the heat of anger flush to my cheeks. "You promised that you would never call me that!" 'Plato' was the derisive name given to me by some of my school-fellows simply because I excelled in history and literature, and because I walked around, as Robbie would say, with a card-catalogue for a mind - "You are the human footnote", he once goaded. But realising that he had touched one of my sensitive spots he put his strong arm around my shoulders and smiled, "I'm sorry Jem, I won't call you that again. Come on, there's something I want to show you up at our castle. Race you!"

As a general rule, our 'castle' was where we met because Robbie had to come up from one side of the hill and I from the other. Robbie and I stood for a moment silhouetted against the rose shot sky around a lowering sun, the horizon vermilion streaked. The Robbie stooped toward a

patch of grass between mossy green and lichen covered stones and spread his hands to reveal a lapwing's nest. Lying in the grassy bowl were four buff-olive and heavily black-speckled eggs.

"Peewit - peewit," we could hear a distant cry. "Give a Gipsy girl a lapwing's nest and she will bare as many children," Robbie said. "Now look Jemmy, don't you go tellin on me," Robbie confided, "but I stole a kiss from Maudie, Tom Tinkler's girl." In my mind's eye, I could see the Nick mist shrouded, eerily silent as the lapwing shells cracked apart to reveal four tiny changelings in place of the chicks.

"It's nearly dark," I said, "and soon mother will be angry at me for staying out so late. You can come home with me, mother doesn't mind you staying and you can sleep in the big bed in my room."

After tea and a wash, we both slid beneath the wild patchwork counterpane covering the feather-bed. Pip stayed the night with mother. Robin said "goodnight matey" and ever so gently brushed my cheek with his rough hand.

Alesandro always said that if a Gipsy left his boots beside your bed he would always return to you. I woke up the next morning to find that Robbie had already gone. And he must have walked home barefoot - because his boots were still at the foot of the bed.

I also had a secret place that not even Pip shared with me. A place to go alone in a wooded patch at the foot of Pendle Hill - my oubliette, place of forgetting. There, I saw him for the first time - the Horned God, protector of all wild creatures and a man's comforter. Not, of course, that I could see him as clearly as all that - he was a fleeting image caught in the corner of the eye. I still feel his presence when I walk alone in the woods. And he has always provided a companion to compensate for the loss of the human kind. Before I left Lancashire, I shared that secret with Robin and took him there. We kicked off our shoes because the ground on which we stood was sacred.

I have always had a best friend. My brother too - until his mate caught a lump of shrapnel in his belly on a foreign battlefield. Pip and I were best friends too. His name was Guy Philip, but everyone called him Pip because that was all that he could make of his own name and because our mother had an affinity for the characters in Dickens' novels. In this instance, the Pip of *Great Expectations*. Pip was two years younger than I and had beautiful auburn hair in which the sun could spark into dance a red flame.

We only had each other for friends and playfellows until we had been in school for several years and I started going about with Robbie. Later, Pip always made friends more easily than I did. With me friendship was too serious a matter to be given lightly. Most of the other chaps found me too moody and complex. Robbie said that he did too but he thought that I was something special so that he didn't give up - and he'd pricked the Romany blood from my finger to mingle with his own.

Pip had a toy fire-engine. Bright red and shiny new - a gift from nan for Christmas - though we celebrated Yule and waited out the cold through Imbolc until the warming of Beltane fires. It was only in later years that I realised how much a symbol of security that red fire-engine was for Pip. He used to toddle up to me with it gleaming under his arm and say, "Is it still nice? There aren't any scratches on it are there, Jemmy? And the colour - it is still bright and shiny isn't it? - Like it was bought in the shop yesterday, almost!"

Pip never talked to anyone but me. If he wanted something or had to express himself he would tug on the cuff of my shirt and whisper in my ear. I would then have to relay his message - I was Pip's medium.

As we got older we ran about with the same group of friends. Pip excelled inmost sports but on horseback or in the water I was definitely his superior. Quite apart from our friends though, we used to have adventures of our own.

One hot summer afternoon we took it into our heads to storm the bastions of a neighbouring orchard, scrumping for apples had an attraction all its' own, even though the trees in our garden bore sweet fruit. Pip was better at climbing trees than I was - heights always made me dizzy. So I peeled off my shirt and gathered up the apples as Pip threw them down.

Then, what should happen but the farmer came charging at us from his back door-step - fully armed! "Run for it, Pip," I howled, and the two of us were off like a shot leaving my shirt and the apples behind. I was the first over the drystone wall but Pip wasn't so lucky. Just as his backside rose up before the plunge to safety, the farmer levelled his shot-gun and pulled the trigger! Pip came down on the other side with a thud and a moan. I held him under the arms most of the way home and sat in the kitchen thinking about my lost shirt and apples while mother picked the buckshot out of Pip's backside, one by one, with a pair of tweezers.

Pip's fire-engine is gone now. I think of its rusty red fragments and I think of that lump of bleeding shrapnel - and I think of the distance that stretches out between us. It is an irremediable loss, as in that of a limb or an eye or the sturdy portion of a still beating heart. A heart that beats time between the gaps left with each parting friendship - Robbie and those that followed him on the open road.

In the autumn and spring, there was kite flying - an enthusiasm that I have kept right down to the present day. When a masterful wind was up and out, Robbie and I would head up to one of the lower pastures beneath the hill with our home-made kites. Robbie always got his kite aloft almost effortlessly and then anchored it to swoop and soar by itself while he came to help me get mine airborne. As it rose higher and higher he gave it back to me to play out the string. How it thrilled to feel the tug on the hand with each new gust of wind. Then, once, the string snapped! My heart leaped to my throat. But Robbie was quick and caught the end of the broken string with one leap - and secured it to the string of his own kite - and there, in a burning blue autumn sky, the two kites played together. They seemed like two souls pulling towards heaven but weighed down by too earthly bodies.

A day came when our fathers, feeling that a few years longer on the face of this planet added to their ability to know what was best, decided that we should pick up our travelling again. We would have new and, sadly, separate worlds to explore and to grow in. My father was taking us to America and Robbie was bound for a land just as distant from our hill.

Robbie arranged to meet me up on the Nick of Pendle the day before we were due to leave for Southampton. He stooped and shoved something in the top of my boot. "Put a sprig of tansy in your boot," he said, "and no matter how far you walk you will never have sore feet."

We talked of many things on that afternoon so long ago now that it seems superfluous to try to recall them. He promised to keep in touch - which he never did. I promised not to forget him either - which I did. Life separated us. Life alone was to blame - not gods, nor men, nor providence, nor fate, nor any of the other rationalities we use to cheat despair.

"Let's have one last go at the slope before we roll down other hills," Robbie laughed.

We locked our arms together and went rolling down the lion's mane - first Robbie on top and then me. The whole of the countryside went spinning by - sea and sky, moor and stream, hill and slope all jumbled together - a kaleidoscope of colour and sensation. It was not without pain - this elation. Every few feet there was a stone or a briar and either one, or the other, or both got it. When we reached the bottom of the hill we staggered about - everything was still in motion around our heads. I lurched toward Robbie who was stabilising faster than I. The tears in my eyes betrayed a regret that I did not know how to label - I still don't.

"Oh, Robbie, let's do it again."

Robbie caught me by the shoulders and laughed. As he took off down the hill in the direction of the Gisburn Road and his family's waiting vardo, he called back over his shoulder, "we will, we will, Jemmy, just as soon as the world stops spinning around!"

Appenòíx

A Romany Herbal

The number of medicinal plants applications known to and used by the Romanies rivals that of any Medieval Herbal.

Make a tea by infusion of one ounce of the bark, root or flower in one pint of water. Drink a wineglassful night and morning of the tea best suited to your particular complaint.

Ointments are made by blending the particular plant or plant extract with unsalted lard.

Poultices can be made into a paste or wrapped in muslin and bandaged over the affected area.

Adder's Tongue	-	Open wounds (crushed and boiled in oil)
Agaric	-	Diarrhoea
Agrimony	-	Coughs
Alder	-	Laxative, jaundice
Ash	-	Laxative (bark), Rheumatoid Arthritis (leaves)
Avens	-	Sore throats, diarrhoea
Barberry	-	Kidney complaints
Bettony	-	Upset stomachs, stings and bites (when made into an ointment)
Blackberry	-	Diarrhoea

Black Currant	-	Sore Throats, catarrh
Bladderwrack	-	Rheumatism (as an embrocation)
Bindweed	-	Worms
Birch	-	Eczema
Bracken	-	Worms, constipation
Brooklime	-	Piles, boils (as a poultice)
Broom	-	Kidney complaints
Buckbean	-	Loss of appetite
Buckthorn Alder	-	Purgative
Burdock	-	Rheumatism
Camomile	-	Debility, stress, hysteria
Carrot (wild)	-	Kidney complaints (the young leaves)
Celandine	-	Corns and warts (application of the juice)
Centaury	-	Tonic, jaundice, constipation
Cherry	-	Chest complaints
Chicory	-	Jaundice
Chivers	-	Head colds
Colts foot	-	Asthma, bronchitis (dried leaves smoked as a tobacco), ulcers, sores, piles (as an ointment)
Comfrey	-	Aids healing broken bones
Couch Grass	-	Fevers
Cowslip	-	Fevers
Cuckoo-pint	-	Bronchitis
Dandelion	-	Rheumatism, Liver complaints (root-roasted also makes a good coffee substitute) Laxative, tonic (leaves)
Elder	-	Colic, Rheumatism, Neuralgia, Boils, Urinary complaints
Eye Bright	-	Coughs, Catarrah, Eye-lotion
Foxglove	-	Fevers

Gentian	-	Heart burn, and Flatulence
Golden rod	-	Gravel, stones, induce vomiting
Ground ivy	-	Internal ulcers, coughs
Groundsel	-	Colic, Inflammation
Hawkweed	-	Convulsions
Hemlock	-	Sores, ulcers (as an ointment)
Henbane	-	Headaches, sleeplessness
Honeysuckle	-	Sore throats (juice of the berries)
Hop	-	Liver and kidney complaints, sciatica, lumbago (as a poultice)
Horehound	-	Coughs, colds
Iceland Moss	-	Loss of appetite
Juniper	-	Flatulence (juice of berries) The wax on the berries' surface makes a good insect repellent
Lily of the Valley	-	Stimulates the heart
Lime	-	Biliousness
Linseed	-	Easy birthing
Lobelia	-	Bronchitis
Loosestrife	-	Diarrhoea
Male fern	-	Worms
Marshmallow	-	Dysentry, sore eyes (as a lotion), sore throats, coughs (as a tea), bites, stings, sore feet (as an ointment)
Meadow-saffron	-	Gout
Meadowsweet	-	Kidney tonic, internal inflammation
Milkwort	-	Chest complaints
Nettles	-	Blood pressure, rashes
Oak	-	Antiseptic, tonic
Parsley	-	Kidney and liver complaints
Pennyroyal	-	Chills, colds, insect repellent
Peppermint	-	Headaches, Flatulence

Pilewort	-	Piles (as an ointment)
Plaintain	-	Piles, bleeding, cuts (leaves)
Raspberry	-	Sore throats (as a gargle)
Red clover	-	Coughs
Red dock	-	Blood purifier
Rhubarb	-	Laxative
Rosemary	-	Stimulates hair growth
Safflower	-	Fevers, menstrual complaints
Saint John's Wort	-	Stress, depression, kidney complaints, catarrah, promotes hair growth
Scabious	-	Pleurisy, internal inflammation
Scurvey grass	-	Skin complaints (eat the fresh leaves)
Soapwort	-	Black eyes (the root)
Solomon's seal	-	Pulmonary complaints, black eyes
Sorrel	-	Fevers
Southernwood	-	Menstrual disorders
Tansy	-	Worms, gout
Thyme (wild)	-	Antiseptic (regarded as unlucky so never brought into the vardo)
Tormentil	-	Diarrhoea
Travellers joy	-	Rheumatism
Valerian	-	Stress, depression, sleeplessness
Violet	-	Poultices
Willow	-	Rheumatic fever, arthritis, rheumatism
Wood sage	-	Kidney and liver complaints, fever
Wormwood	-	Aids digestion
Yarrow	-	Colds, fever

Select Bibliography

As memory does not always hold the door, I have consulted a select number of books for colour and veracity.

Ainsworth, William Harrison *Rookwood*, 1834
Ainsworth, William Harrison *Mervin Clitheroe* 1857
Anon, *Gypsies and Other Travellers* (HMSO) 1967
Borrow, George, *Lavengro* 1900
Borrow, George, *The Romany Rye* 1900
Boswell, Sylvester Gordon, *The Book of Boswell* 1970
Clebert, Jean-Paul, *The Gypsies* 1963
Cutriss, Frank, *Romany Life* 1915
Dickens, Charles *The Old Curiosity Shop* 1848
Dodds, Norman *Gypsies, Didikois and Other Travellers* 1966
Duff, Charles, *A Mysterious People* 1965
Farre, Rowena, *Seal Morning* 1957
Farre, Rowena, *A Time From This World* 1962
Leland, Charles G, *The English Gypsies and Their Language* 1874
Petulengro, Gypsy, *Romany Remedies and Recipes* 1935
Simson, Walter, *A History of the Gypsies* 1865
Versey-Fitzgerald, Brian, *Gypsies of Britain* 1973
Ward-Jackson, C.H. & Harvey, Denis E. *The English Gypsy Caravan* 1972
Webb, G.C.E., *Gypsies: The Secret People* 1960
Woodcock, Henry, *The Gipsies* 1865

A selection of other Capall Bann titles. Free catalogue available.

The Eildon Tree - Romany Language and Lore by Michael Hoadley

With *A Romany Tapestry* this forms the most complete (and personal) survey of the Romanies in the 20th century making the great quantity of material gathered through the author's life available to those with an interest in, and affection for, this unique people. *The Eildon Tree* includes traditional Romany tales, a comprehensive dictionary detailing this long-surviving oral tradition which still survives largely as a secret language, Romany phrases and proverbs, songs and sections on a Romany Yule and Sahmain. ISBN 186163 097 2

Magical Guardians - Exploring the Spirit & Nature of Trees
by Philip Heselton

This is a book about trees, but a book with a difference, for it acknowledges trees to be wise beings who can teach us much if we approach them in the right way. This book shows how to go about it, revealing the origins of our awakening interest in - and love for - trees. Trees have a spiritual nature, and opening up to this spirit has been a constant feature in human society. Through practical guidance, this book gives hints on how we can make that contact for ourselves. The personalities of the ancient trees - our Magical Guardians - are explored, and the book reveals how we can start to acquire some of their deeper meanings. ISBN 1 86163 057 3   £11.95

Tree: Essence, Spirit and Teacher   by Simon & Sue Lilly

Trees are the creators and maintainers of our reality. In every tradition their spiritual strength has been clearly recognised. Sue and Simon Lilly, developers of *"Green Man Tree Essences"*, share their experiences and describe a wide range of techniques by which we can come into a direct and powerful relationship with the Tree Kingdoms. Emphasis is placed on establishing a personal experience through which the teachings of the Tree Spirits can become apparent. Subjects covered include: The metaphysical reality of trees, Tree essences and how to use them; Meeting the Spirits - methods of communication; Tree Teacher Techniques; Attunements to forty different trees; Coming into the presence of tree energies through initiation, and an exploration of some powerful Tree Teachers. This is the first volume in the *"Tree Seer"* series. ISBN 18163 084 0   £15.95

Tree: Essence of Healing   by Simon & Sue Lilly

The tree is the epitome of balance and stability. Each tree is a window through which we can experience the seamless wholeness of creation, enabling us to re-integrate and repair those aspects of ourselves that have become isolated and damaged. Through the powerful medium of tree essences we have access to the great healing potential of the Tree Kingdoms. This volume explores the qualities of wholeness that trees and tree essences can bring back to the Human Kingdom. Included is a survey of essences and how they work; different ways of healing with trees; an exploration of trees and their healing qualities. ISBN 18163 0816   £14.95

The Enchanted Forest - The Magical Lore of Trees by Yvonne Aburrow

Fascinating & truly unique - a comprehensive guide to the magical, medicinal & craft uses, mythology, folklore, symbolism & weatherlore of trees. There are chapters on trees in myth & legend, tree spirits, trees in ritual magic, trees & alphabets (runes & Ogham) & weather lore. These chapters are followed by a comprehensive 'herbal index' with in-depth coverage of individual trees from acacia to aspen, wayfaring tree to willow. Profusely illustrated. ISBN 1898307 083   £10.95

FREE DETAILED CATALOGUE

A detailed illustrated catalogue is available on request, SAE or International Postal Coupon appreciated. **Titles can be ordered direct from Capall Bann, post free in the UK** (cheque or PO with order) or from good bookshops and specialist outlets. Titles currently available include:

Auguries and Omens - The Magical Lore of Birds by Yvonne Aburrow
Caer Sidhe - Celtic Astrology and Astronomy by Michael Bayley
Call of the Horned Piper by Nigel Jackson
Celtic Lore & Druidic Ritual by Rhiannon Ryall
Earth Dance - A Year of Pagan Rituals by Jan Brodie
Earth Magic by Margaret McArthur
Enchanted Forest - The Magical Lore of Trees by Yvonne Aburrow
Familiars - Animal Powers of Britain by Anna Franklin
Healing Book (The) by Chris Thomas
Healing Homes by Jennifer Dent
Herbcraft - Shamanic & Ritual Use of Herbs by S Lavender & Anna Franklin
In Search of Herne the Hunter by Eric Fitch
Magical Guardians - Exploring the Spirit & Nature of Trees by PHeselton
Magical Lore of Cats by Marion Davies
Magical Lore of Herbs by Marion Davies
Patchwork of Magic by Julia Day
Psychic Self Defence - Real Solutions by Jan Brodie
Sacred Animals by Gordon MacLellan
Sacred Grove - The Mysteries of the Forest by Yvonne Aburrow
Sacred Geometry by Nigel Pennick
Sacred Lore of Horses The by Marion Davies
Secret Places of the Goddess by Philip Heselton
Talking to the Earth by Gordon Maclellan
Taming the Wolf - Full Moon Meditations by Steve Hounsome

Capall Bann is owned and run by people actively involved in many of the areas in which we publish. Our list is expanding rapidly so do contact us for details on the latest releases.

Capall Bann Publishing, Freshfields, Chieveley, Berks, RG20 8TF